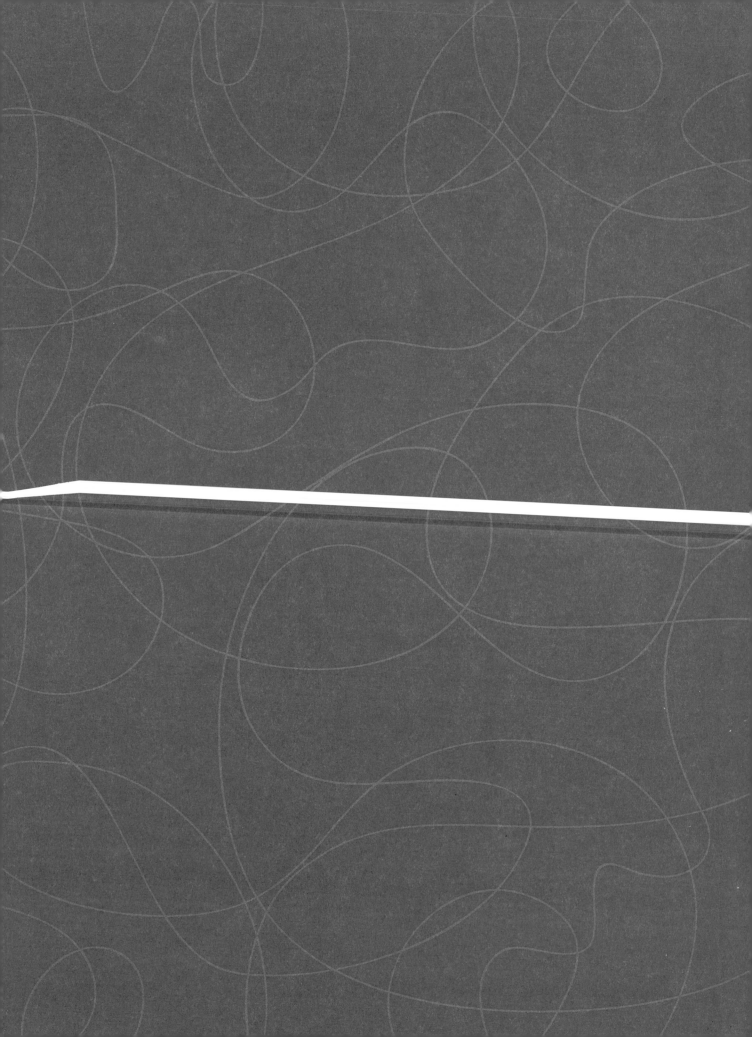

CALIFORNIA

SRA Imagine It!

Level 4 · Book 1

Themes

Risks and Consequences

Nature's Delicate Balance

A Changing State

SRA Imagine It!

CALIFORNIA

Level 4
Book 1

Program Authors

Carl Bereiter

Andy Biemiller

Joe Campione

Doug Fuchs

Lynn Fuchs

Steve Graham

Karen Harris

Karen Hayashi

Jan Hirshberg

Anne McKeough

Peter Pannell

Michael Pressley

Marsha Roit

Marlene Scardamalia

Marcy Stein

Gerald H. Treadway Jr.

McGraw Hill SRA

Columbus, OH

Acknowledgments

Grateful acknowledgement is given to the following publishers and copyright owners for permissions granted to reprint selections from their publications. All possible care has been taken to trace ownership and secure permission for each selection included. In case of any errors or omissions, the Publisher will be pleased to make suitable acknowledgements in future editions.

RISKS AND CONSEQUENCES

Chapter 10 from ISLAND OF THE BLUE DOLPHINS. Copyright © 1960, renewed 1988 by Scott O'Dell. Reprinted by permission of Houghton Mifflin Company. All rights reserved.

From TWO TICKETS TO FREEDOM. Text © 1971 Florence B. Freedman, illustrations © 1971 Ezra Jack Keats. Reprinted with permission of School Specialty Publishing. All rights reserved.

"Mrs. Frisby and the Crow" reprinted with the permission of Atheneum Books for Young Readers, an imprint of Simon & Schuster Children's Publishing Division from MRS. FRISBY AND THE RATS OF NIMH by Robert C. O'Brien. Copyright © 1971 Robert C. O'Brien; copyright renewed 1999 Christopher Conly, Jane Leslie Conly, Kate Conly and Sarah Conly.

"Langston Hughes: Poet of the People" by Mary Satchell from PLAYS OF BLACK AMERICANS © 2003 and PLAYS, The Drama Magazine for Young People © October 1993, reprinted with the permission of the publisher PLAYS/ Sterling partners, Inc., PO Box 600160, Newton, MA 02460.

English-Language Arts Content Standards for California Public Schools reproduced by permission, California Department of Education, CDE Press, 1430 N Street, Suite 3207, Sacramento, CA 95814.

"Daedalus and Icarus" reprinted with the permission of Margaret K. McElderry Books, an imprint of Simon & Schuster Children's Publishing Division from GREEK MYTHS by Geraldine McCaughrean, illustrated by Emma Chichester Clark. Text copyright © 1992 Geraldine McCaughrean. Illustrations copyright © 1992 Emma Chichester Clark.

"The Dream Keeper" from COLLECTED POEMS by Langston Hughes, copyright © 1994 by The Estate of Langston Hughes. Used by permission of Alfred A Knopf, a division of Random House Inc.

"Freedom" from COLLECTED POEMS by Langston Hughes, copyright © 1994 by The Estate of Langston Hughes. Used by permission of Alfred A Knopf, a division of Random House Inc.

"Dreams" from COLLECTED POEMS by Langston Hughes, copyright © 1994 by The Estate of Langston Hughes. Used by permission of Alfred A Knopf, a division of Random House Inc.

NATURE'S DELICATE BALANCE

"The Snowflake" by Neil Waldman. Copyright © 2003 by Neil Waldman. Reprinted with the permission of Lerner Publishing Group, Inc. All rights reserved. No part of this text excerpt may be used or reproduced in any manner whatsoever without the prior written permission of Lerner Publishing Group, Inc.

ENERGY MAKES THINGS HAPPEN by Kimberly Brubaker Bradley. COPYRIGHT © 2003. Published by arrangement with HarperCollins Children's Books, a division of HarperCollins Publishers. All rights reserved.

WHO EATS WHAT?: FOOD CHAINS AND FOOD WEBS by Patricia Lauber. COPYRIGHT © 1995. Published by arrangement with HarperCollins Children's Books, a division of HarperCollins Publishers. All rights reserved.

WHAT ROT! Copyright © 1996 by Elizabeth Hennefrund. All rights reserved.

THE GREAT KAPOK TREE: A TALE OF THE AMAZON RAIN FOREST, copyright © 1990 by Lynne Cherry, reprinted by permission of Harcourt, Inc. This material may not be reproduced in any form or by any means without the prior written permission of the publisher.

"Yellow Leaf" by Frederick Zydek. Reprinted by permission of CRICKET magazine, September 2000, copyright, © 2000 by Frederick Zydek.

"Mold, Mold" from SOMETHING BIG HAS BEEN HERE by Jack Prelutsky. TEXT COPYRIGHT © 1980 BY JACK PRELUTSKY. Used by permission of HarperCollins Publishers.

"Circle of Songs" by Cynthia A. Porter. Reprinted by permission of CRICKET magazine, April 2004, copyright, © 2004 by Cynthia A. Porter.

A CHANGING STATE

"The First Californians" from CALIFORNIA (AMERICA THE BEAUTIFUL) by Ann Heinrichs. © 1998 by Children's Press ® a division of Grolier Publishing Co., Inc. All rights reserved. Reprinted by permission of Children's Press, an imprint of Scholastic Library Publishing, Inc.

From "STRIKING IT RICH The Story of the California Gold Rush" by Stephen Krensky. Text Copyright © 1996 by Stephen Krensky. Used by permission of The Gersh Agency.

A COVERED WAGON GIRL: THE DIARY OF SALLIE HESTER 1849–1850 by Sallie Hester © 2000 by Capstone Press. All rights reserved.

From THE EARTH DRAGON AWAKES by Laurence Yep © 2006. Used by permission of HarperCollins Publishers.

"In and Around Los Angeles" from CITY OF ANGELS: IN AND AROUND LOS ANGELES by Julie Jaskol and Brian Lewis, copyright © 1999 by Julie Jaskol and Brian Lewis, text. Used by permission of Dutton Children's Books, A Division of Penguin Young Readers Group, A Member of Penguin Group (USA) Inc., 345 Hudson Street, New York, NY 10014. All rights reserved.

"California Missions" by Ann Whitford Paul. Used by permission of the author.

"A Gold Miner's Tale" from WE THE PEOPLE by Bobbi Katz. COPYRIGHT © 2000 by BOBBI KATZ. Used by permission of HarperCollins Children's Publishing.

SRAonline.com

 SRA

Copyright © 2009 by SRA/McGraw-Hill.

All rights reserved. No part of the this publication may be reproduced or distributed in any form or by any means, or stored in a database or retrieval system, without the prior written consent of The McGraw-Hill Companies, Inc., including, but not limited to, network storage or transmission, or broadcast for distance learning. An Open Court Curriculum.

Printed in the United States of America.

Send all inquiries to this address:
SRA/McGraw-Hill
4400 Easton Commons
Columbus, OH 43219

ISBN: 978-0-07-621380-1
MHID: 0-07-621380-3

2 3 4 5 6 7 8 9 RRW 13 12 11 10 09 08

The McGraw·Hill Companies

Program Authors

Carl Bereiter, Ph.D.
University of Toronto

Andrew Biemiller, Ph.D.
University of Toronto

Joe Campione, Ph.D.
University of California, Berkeley

Doug Fuchs, Ph.D.
Vanderbilt University

Lynn Fuchs, Ph.D.
Vanderbilt University

Steve Graham, Ph.D.
Vanderbilt University

Karen Harris, Ph.D.
Vanderbilt University

Karen Hayashi
Former Administrator,
Elk Grove Unified School District,
Elk Grove, California

Jan Hirshberg, Ed.D.
Reading Specialist

Anne McKeough, Ph.D.
University of Calgary

Peter Pannell, Principal
Eliot Middle School,
Altadena, California

Michael Pressley, Ph.D.
Michigan State University

Marsha Roit, Ph.D.
National Reading Consultant

Marlene Scardamalia, Ph.D.
University of Toronto

Marcy Stein, Ph.D.
University of Washington, Tacoma

Gerald H. Treadway, Jr., Ed.D.
San Diego State University

Unit 1 Table of Contents

Risks and Consequences

Nature's Delicate Balance

Unit 3

Table of Contents

A Changing State

Risks and Consequences

Have you ever taken a risk? What happened? We take risks every day—every time we decide to do something or not to do it. How do you decide which risks are worth taking?

Theme Connection

Look at the photograph.

- Why is the truck crossing the bridge?
- Do you think the bridge can support this truck?
- How does this illustrate taking a risk?

BIG
Idea

Why do people
take risks?

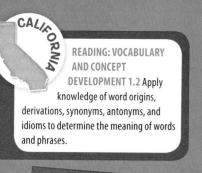

READING: VOCABULARY AND CONCEPT DEVELOPMENT 1.2 Apply knowledge of word origins, derivations, synonyms, antonyms, and idioms to determine the meaning of words and phrases.

Read the story to find the meanings of these words, which are also in "Island of the Blue Dolphins":

◆ idly
◆ tides
◆ companions
◆ pursued
◆ dozed
◆ lacking
◆ fiber
◆ headland
◆ lessened
◆ sandspit
◆ seeping
◆ bow

Vocabulary Development

Word Analysis gives us clues about a word's meaning. Look at the word *idly*. Review the suffix *-ly* and the root *idle* to find the word's meaning.

Vocabulary

Warm-Up

Today was not a day for idly strolling along the beach, watching the tides. Even though they were sisters, Mika and Yuki were close companions. They had always pursued adventure!

The beach was empty, and their father had dozed off. The sisters decided to pretend they were stranded on an island, lacking the comforts of home.

"It's been five days since we've had a good meal!" moaned Yuki.

"Let's go find some real food," announced Mika. "I'll tie this red piece of fiber to a tree so we can find our way back," she said.

They ran to the other side of the headland. A large group of banana trees swayed gently in the wind.

"The winds seem to have **lessened**," Yuki said. "Yesterday, I kept getting sand in my face."

Mika laughed and rattled one of the trees. It did not budge.

The two girls pushed the tree back and forth. Finally, some bananas broke free and landed on the sand.

They carried their treasure to a nearby **sandspit**. Yuki squeezed too hard while opening the peel, and her banana starting **seeping** through her hands.

Suddenly, they saw something not too far up the beach.

"Oh, look!" Yuki said. "A ship has come to rescue us!"

"That looks like Dad standing on the **bow**, waving to us!" said Mika.

"Who's hungry for breakfast?" Dad called.

Vocabulary Word Play

Work with a partner. On a sheet of paper, write one of the words in the diamond. Think of other words that explain its meaning. Write these words in the boxes. When you have finished, compare webs with your partner. Discuss why you chose certain words.

Give examples!

Concept Vocabulary

This lesson's concept word is *dilemma.* A *dilemma* is a situation in which each choice looks equally bad. Characters in stories and in movies often face dilemmas. It makes the story more suspenseful and exciting. Think of one of your favorite book or movie characters who faced a dilemma. What choice did the character eventually make, and why? Think of a time when *you* faced a dilemma. Share your experience with a classmate.

15

Genre

Realistic Fiction involves stories with characters and settings that are true to life and events that could really happen.

Comprehension Skill

☆ **Author's Point of View** As you read, understand who is telling the story. Ask what a particular point of view's strengths and weaknesses are and whether the point of view allows you to see the "whole" story.

Island of the Blue

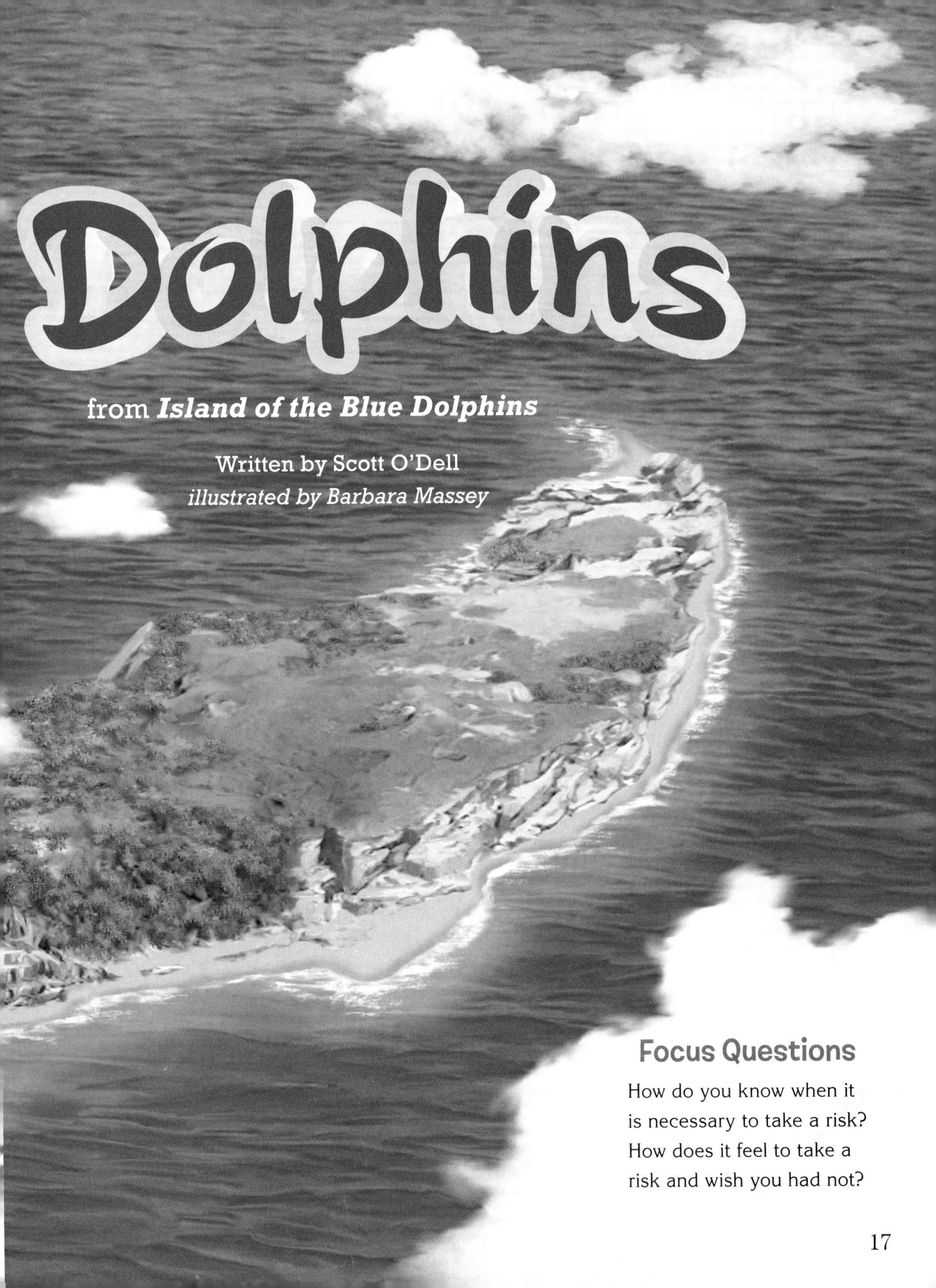

Dolphins

from *Island of the Blue Dolphins*

Written by Scott O'Dell
illustrated by Barbara Massey

Focus Questions

How do you know when it is necessary to take a risk? How does it feel to take a risk and wish you had not?

17

With the help of the white man's ship, Karana's people have fled their island to escape the Aleuts, their enemies. In their haste Karana is left behind on the island. As she waits for a ship to return to rescue her, Karana's hopes begin to fade.

Summer is the best time on the Island of the Blue Dolphins. The sun is warm then and the winds blow milder out of the west, sometimes out of the south.

It was during these days that the ship might return and now I spent most of my time on the rock, looking out from the high headland into the east, toward the country where my people had gone, across the sea that was never-ending.

Once while I watched I saw a small object which I took to be the ship, but a stream of water rose from it and I knew that it was a whale spouting. During those summer days I saw nothing else.

The first storm of winter ended my hopes. If the white men's ship were coming for me it would have come during the time of good weather. Now I would have to wait until winter was gone, maybe longer.

The thought of being alone on the island while so many suns rose from the sea and went slowly back into the sea filled my heart with loneliness. I had not felt so lonely before because I was sure that the ship would return as Matasaip had said it would. Now my hopes were dead. Now I was really alone. I could not eat much, nor could I sleep without dreaming terrible dreams.

The storm blew out of the north, sending big waves against the island and winds so strong that I was unable to stay on the rock. I moved my bed to the foot of the rock and for protection kept a fire going throughout the night. I slept there five times. The first night the dogs came and stood outside the ring made by the fire. I killed three of them with arrows, but not the leader, and they did not come again.

On the sixth day, when the storm had ended, I went to the place where the canoes had been hidden, and let myself down over the cliff. This part of the shore was sheltered from the wind and I found the canoes just as they had been left. The dried food was still good, but the water was stale, so I went back to the spring and filled a fresh basket.

I had decided during the days of the storm, when I had given up hope of seeing the ship, that I would take one of the canoes and go to the country that lay toward the east. I remembered how Kimki, before he had gone, had asked the advice of his ancestors who had lived many ages in the past, who had come to the island from that country, and likewise the advice of Zuma, the medicine man who held power over the wind and the seas. But these things I could not do, for Zuma had been killed by the Aleuts, and in all my life I had never been able to speak with the dead, though many times I had tried.

Yet I cannot say that I was really afraid as I stood there on the shore. I knew that my ancestors had crossed the sea in their canoes, coming from that place which lay beyond. Kimki, too had crossed the sea. I was not nearly so skilled with a canoe as these men, but I must say that whatever might befall me on the endless waters did not trouble me. It meant far less than the thought of staying on the island alone, without a home or companions, pursued by wild dogs, where everything reminded me of those who were dead and those who had gone away.

Of the four canoes stored there against the cliff, I chose the smallest, which was still very heavy because it could carry six people. The task that faced me was to push it down the rocky shore and into the water, a distance four or five times its length.

This I did by first removing all the large rocks in front of the canoe. I then filled in all these holes with pebbles and along this path laid down long strips of kelp, making a slippery bed. The shore was steep and once I got the canoe to move with its own weight, it slid down the path and into the water.

The sun was in the west when I left the shore. The sea was calm behind the high cliffs. Using the two-bladed paddle I quickly skirted the south part of the island. As I reached the sandspit the wind struck. I was paddling from the back of the canoe because you can go faster kneeling there, but I could not handle it in the wind.

Kneeling in the middle of the canoe, I paddled hard and did not pause until I had gone through the tides that run fast around the sandspit. There were many small waves and I was soon wet, but as I came out from behind the spit the spray lessened and the waves grew long and rolling. Though it would have been easier to go the way they slanted, this would have taken me in the wrong direction. I therefore kept them on my left hand, as well as the island, which grew smaller and smaller, behind me.

At dusk I looked back. The Island of the Blue Dolphins had disappeared. This was the first time that I felt afraid.

There were only hills and valleys of water around me now. When I was in a valley I could see nothing and when the canoe rose out of it, only the ocean stretching away and away.

Night fell and I drank from the basket. The water cooled my throat.

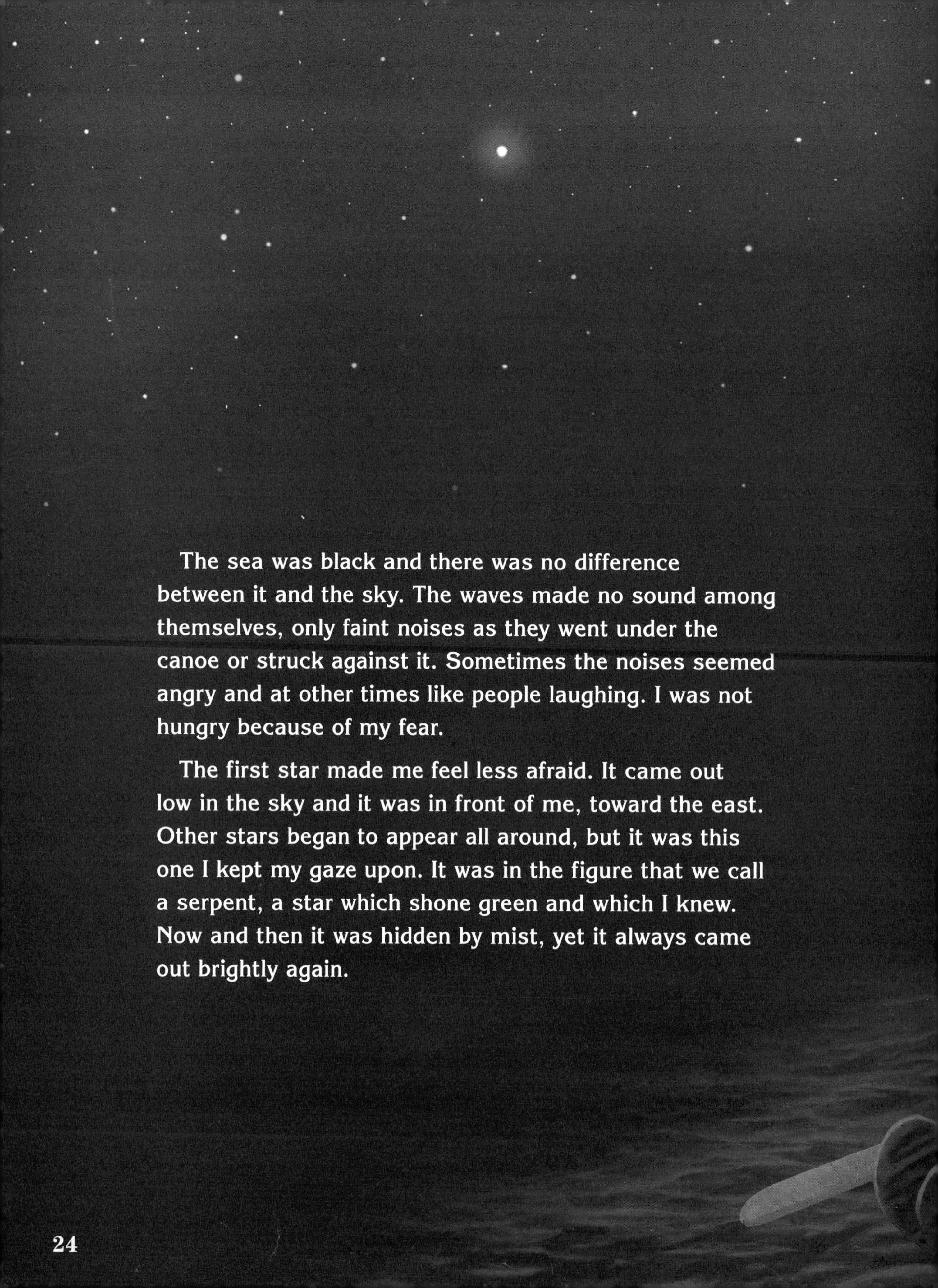

The sea was black and there was no difference between it and the sky. The waves made no sound among themselves, only faint noises as they went under the canoe or struck against it. Sometimes the noises seemed angry and at other times like people laughing. I was not hungry because of my fear.

The first star made me feel less afraid. It came out low in the sky and it was in front of me, toward the east. Other stars began to appear all around, but it was this one I kept my gaze upon. It was in the figure that we call a serpent, a star which shone green and which I knew. Now and then it was hidden by mist, yet it always came out brightly again.

Without this star I would have been lost, for the waves never changed. They came always from the same direction and in a manner that kept pushing me away from the place I wanted to reach. For this reason the canoe made a path in the black water like a snake. But somehow I kept moving toward the star which shone in the east.

This star rose high and then I kept the North Star on my left hand, the one we call "the star that does not move." The wind grew quiet. Since it always died down when the night was half over, I knew how long I had been traveling and how far away the dawn was.

About this time I found that the canoe was leaking. Before dark I had emptied one of the baskets in which food was stored and used it to dip out the water that came over the sides. The water that now moved around my knees was not from the waves.

I stopped paddling and worked with the basket until the bottom of the canoe was almost dry. Then I searched around, feeling in the dark along the smooth planks, and found the place near the bow where the water was seeping through a crack as long as my hand and the width of a finger. Most of the time it was out of the sea, but it leaked whenever the canoe dipped forward in the waves.

The places between the planks were filled with black pitch which we gather along the shore. Lacking this, I tore a piece of fiber from my skirt and pressed it into the crack, which held back the water.

Dawn broke in a clear sky and as the sun came out of the waves I saw that it was far off on my left. During the night I had drifted south of the place I wished to go, so I changed my direction and paddled along the path made by the rising sun.

There was no wind on this morning and the long waves went quietly under the canoe. I therefore moved faster than during the night.

I was very tired, but more hopeful than I had been since I left the island. If the good weather did not change I would cover many leagues before dark. Another night and another day might bring me within sight of the shore toward which I was going.

Not long after dawn, while I was thinking of this strange place and what it would look like, the canoe began to leak again. This crack was between the same planks, but was a larger one and close to where I was kneeling.

The fiber I tore from my skirt and pushed into the crack held back most of the water which seeped in whenever the canoe rose and fell with the waves. Yet I could see that the planks were weak from one end to the other, probably from the canoe being stored so long in the sun, and that they might open along their whole length if the waves grew rougher.

It was suddenly clear to me that it was dangerous to go on. The voyage would take two more days, perhaps longer. By turning back to the island I would not have nearly so far to travel.

Still I could not make up my mind to do so. The sea was calm and I had come far. The thought of turning back after all this labor was more than I could bear. Even greater was the thought of the deserted island I would return to, of living there alone and forgotten. For how many suns and how many moons?

The canoe drifted idly on the calm sea while these thoughts went over and over in my mind, but when I saw the water seeping through the crack again, I picked up the paddle. There was no choice except to turn back toward the island.

I knew that only by the best of fortune would I ever reach it.

The wind did not blow until the sun was overhead. Before that time I covered a good distance, pausing only when it was necessary to dip water from the canoe. With the wind I went more slowly and had to stop more often because of the water spilling over the sides, but the leak did not grow worse.

This was my first good fortune. The next was when a swarm of dolphins appeared. They came swimming out of the west, but as they saw the canoe they turned around in a great circle and began to follow me. They swam up slowly and so close that I could see their eyes, which are large and the color of the ocean. Then they swam on ahead of the canoe, crossing back and forth in front of it, diving in and out, as if they were weaving a piece of cloth with their broad snouts.

Dolphins are animals of good omen. It made me happy to have them swimming around the canoe, and though my hands had begun to bleed from the chafing of the paddle, just watching them made me forget the pain. I was very lonely before they appeared, but now I felt that I had friends with me and did not feel the same.

The blue dolphins left me shortly before dusk. They left as quickly as they had come, going on into the west, but for a long time I could see the last of the sun shining on them. After night fell I could still see them in my thoughts and it was because of this that I kept on paddling when I wanted to lie down and sleep.

More than anything, it was the blue dolphins that took me back home.

Fog came with the night, yet from time to time I could see the star that stands high in the west, the red star called Magat which is part of the figure that looks like a crawfish and is known by that name. The crack in the planks grew wider so I had to stop often to fill it with fiber and to dip out the water.

The night was very long, longer than the night before.
Twice I dozed kneeling there in the canoe, though I was
more afraid than I had ever been. But the morning broke
clear and in front of me lay the dim line of the island like
a great fish sunning itself on the sea.

I reached it before the sun was high, the sandspit and
its tides that bore me into the shore. My legs were stiff
from kneeling and as the canoe struck the sand I fell
when I rose to climb out. I crawled through the
shallow water and up the beach. There I lay for
a long time, hugging the sand in happiness.

I was too tired to think of the wild dogs.
Soon I fell asleep.

Meet the Author

Scott O'Dell

When O'Dell was born, Los Angeles was still an Old West town. His family lived in many different places in California. For a short time, they lived on an island. O'Dell went to four different colleges. He first wrote books for adults, but when he wrote *Island of the Blue Dolphins*, he realized it was a good book for children. O'Dell's love of the sea and the people of the West come through in his stories.

Meet the Illustrator

Barbara Massey

Massey knew she wanted to be an illustrator when she was fourteen years old. She enjoyed drawing more than anything else. She likes to draw "living things like animals, people, trees, plants, and scenery." Now she draws in a small studio in her house, where she has neatly arranged her computer and her drawing and painting supplies. She also has a bed for her pets so they can sleep beside her while she works. She has a miniature poodle named Chico and a tabby cat named Kitten.

READING: STRUCTURAL FEATURES OF LITERATURE 3.2 Identify the main events of the plot, their causes, and the influence of each event on future actions.

Theme Connections

Discuss

Within the Selection

1. Why does Karana take the canoe away from the Island of the Blue Dolphins by herself?

2. What are the possible consequences of this risk?

Beyond the Selection

3. What risks have you or someone you know taken recently? What were the consequences?

4. Why did you or that person take the risk?

Write

Describe a time you took a risk. What was at risk? Was the outcome worth the risk?

Read

To learn more about dolphins, look for books and magazine articles about dolphins to read on your own.

CALIFORNIA

SCIENCE: PHYSICAL SCIENCES 1.g. Students know electrical energy can be converted to heat, light, and motion.

Science Link

The Tesla Coil

Genre

Expository Text tells people something. It contains facts about real people, things, or events.

Text Feature

Diagrams are drawings that are used to explain how something works.

Some say it was because he was born in a lightning storm. Others think he just loved science. Whatever the reason, Nikola Tesla spent his life working with electricity. In fact, in the late 1890s, he made a machine that allowed electricity to jump from one point to another. His invention is known as the Tesla coil.

Before the coil, electricity could only move through connected wires. But the Tesla coil was not a closed system. It had an empty space between two points, or towers. The two towers then built up such high electrical charges that giant sparks would leap across the gap. It looked just like lightning. The Tesla coil showed that energy could move across open space.

The Tesla coil also showed people how high-voltage energy can be changed into motion. Sometimes scientists would even wear metal suits and stand in the gap between two Tesla coils. When the energy moved from one side to the other, lightning sparks bounced off the suits, leaving the scientists unharmed. Scientists who demonstrated this were careful that an accident did not befall them.

Many of Tesla's inventions are still in use today. Tesla worked with radio frequency waves to invent the radio. He also made speedometers and electrical generators.

Tesla believed that radio waves could see a ship's movement. He was right. Later, his idea became known as RADAR (Radio Detection and Ranging). Tesla also worked with gas-filled lamps, which later became fluorescent lighting. Even when people thought he was misguided, Tesla pursued his ideas.

Think Link

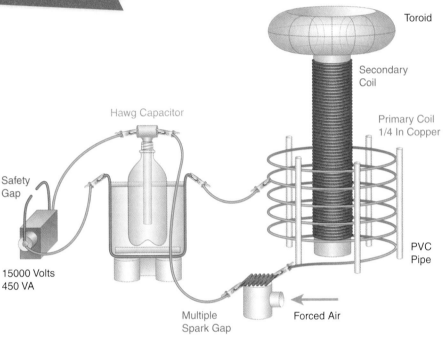

Toroid

Secondary Coil

Primary Coil 1/4 In Copper

Hawg Capacitor

Safety Gap

15000 Volts 450 VA

PVC Pipe

Multiple Spark Gap

Forced Air

1. Describe what a Tesla coil demonstrated to scientists.

2. How did the Tesla coil show that energy could be transferred into motion?

3. Have you ever seen something like the Tesla coil before?

WebLink

CALIFORNIA

Visit **www.ImagineItReading.com/ AtHome** for more information about Tesla coils.

Apply

Diagrams As you work on your investigation, think about how diagrams are used to explain how something works.

READING: VOCABULARY AND CONCEPT DEVELOPMENT 1.2 Apply knowledge of word origins, derivations, synonyms, antonyms, and idioms to determine the meaning of words and phrases. 1.3 Use knowledge of root words to determine the meaning of unknown words within a passage.

Read the story to preview the vocabulary:

- ✦ agitated
- ✦ escorted
- ✦ hurdle
- ✦ concealed
- ✦ ownership
- ✦ hastened
- ✦ preyed
- ✦ shuddered
- ✦ despairing
- ✦ delivered
- ✦ flickering
- ✦ sympathetic

Vocabulary Development

Context Clues are hints in the text that help you find the meanings of words. Define the words *concealed* and *despairing*.

Vocabulary
Warm-Up

Carson's family had one rule when they went camping: "Never leave the campsite alone." One night, as his parents prepared supper, Carson asked his older sister Sam to go for a walk with him.

"No, thanks," she said, barely looking up from her book. She seemed agitated.

Sam made him so mad sometimes. "I will just go by myself," he grumbled. After all, he didn't need to be escorted by his sister.

He tiptoed around the camper and went into the woods. Suddenly, he saw two deer cross the path and jump over a hurdle created by a fallen tree just 20 feet ahead. Seconds later, they were concealed by trees.

Carson left the path and followed the deer. They did not even know he was there! When the deer settled down to rest, he decided to head back.

He started walking and began to panic. Where was the path? All he could see were trees. There were no buildings or signs of ownership. Carson hastened forward. Was he going in the wrong direction?

How long had he been gone? It was starting to get dark. He wondered what animals preyed on children who did not listen to their parents. Carson shuddered at the thought of being alone in the woods at night. "Why didn't I listen to Mom and Dad?" he moaned in a despairing voice. "I would give anything to be delivered from this mess!"

"Mom! Dad!" he yelled. "Can you hear me?" Nothing. He walked and walked but could not find the trail. It was so dark now that he could not see. He sat down against a tree and began to cry.

Just then, he saw a flickering light. "Son, is your name Carson?" said a sympathetic voice.

Carson looked up and saw two forest rangers. They were holding flashlights. He lowered his head. He had some explaining to do.

Vocabulary Word Play

On a separate sheet of paper, write original sentences using six of the vocabulary words. Then think of a synonym for each vocabulary word, and rewrite the sentences using the synonyms correctly. Read your sentences to your partner.

Concept Vocabulary

This lesson's concept word is **resolute.** *Resolute* means "marked by firm determination." Think of a time when you were firmly determined to do something. What was it? Why do you think you were so resolute? Now describe a time when you were the *opposite* of resolute.

CALIFORNIA

READING:
COMPREHENSION AND
ANALYSIS OF GRADE-
LEVEL-APPROPRIATE TEXT 2.4
Evaluate new information and hypotheses
by testing them against known
information and ideas.

Genre

A **biography**
is the story of a real
person's life that is told by
another person.

Comprehension Strategy

Making Connections
As you read the
selection, make connections
between what you already
know from previous
experience and what you
are reading.

Two Tickets to Freedom

from *Two Tickets to Freedom:*
The True Story of Ellen and William Craft,
Fugitive Slaves

by Florence B. Freedman
illustrated by Doris Ettlinger

Focus Questions

Is it sometimes riskier to do nothing?
What is important enough to you to
make you risk your life?

Among the many slaves in Georgia in 1848 were a young couple named William and Ellen Craft. Ellen was a maid and William a skilled cabinetmaker. Their lives were not as harsh as those of many other slaves, but the desire to be free never left them. However, escaping would be difficult!

William had been saving money for tickets to escape. He had a plan for himself and Ellen, who was light-skinned enough to pass for white. Ellen would dress up as an injured man, bandaging her face to further disguise the fact that she was a woman, and bandaging her right arm and hand to prevent anyone from asking her to write. She would then travel with William as her slave.

Their journey would include a train ride to Fredericksburg, Virginia, followed by a boat trip to Washington, D.C., and finally a train ride to Philadelphia, the first stop on the Underground Railroad.

By the time they left the train in Fredericksburg and boarded a ship for Washington, D.C., William and Ellen felt sure they were safe. They were unaware that the most difficult part of their daring escape was just around the corner. Would they ever make it to Philadelphia?

In a few minutes, the ship landed at Washington, and there William and Ellen took a carriage to the train for Baltimore, the last slave port they were to see. They had left their cottage on Wednesday morning, the 21st of December. It was Christmas Eve, December 24, 1848, when they arrived in Baltimore.

William and Ellen were more tense than ever. They were so near their goal . . . yet they knew that officials in Baltimore were particularly watchful to prevent slaves from escaping across the border to Pennsylvania and freedom.

William settled his "master" in a first-class carriage on the train and went to the car in which blacks traveled. Before he entered, a Yankee officer stopped him, saying sternly, "Where are you going, boy?"

"Philadelphia, sir," William replied humbly.

"What are you going there for?" asked the officer.

"I am traveling with my master who is in another carriage, sir."

"I think you had better get him out, and be quick about it, because the train will soon be starting," the officer ordered. "It is against the rules to let any man take a slave past here unless he can satisfy them in the office that he has a right to take him along." The officer moved on, leaving William on the platform.

William's heart was beating furiously. To have come so far—and now this! How would Ellen be able to prove ownership? He consoled himself with the thought that God, who had been so good as to allow them to come this far, would not let them be turned aside now.

William hastened into the car to tell his master the bad news. "Mr. Johnson," seated comfortably in the railroad car, smiled at him. They were so near their destination.

"How are you feeling, sir?" asked William.

"Much better," answered his "master." "Thank God we are getting on so nicely."

"Not so nicely, sir, I am sorry to say," William said. "You must leave the train and convince the officials that I am your slave."

"Mr. Johnson" shuddered.

"Good heavens!" he whispered. "Is it possible that we will be sent back into slavery?"

They were silent for a few despairing moments. Then they left the train and made their way to the office.

Ellen summoned her last bit of courage.

"Do you wish to see me, sir?" "Mr. Johnson" asked the man who appeared to be the chief officer.

"Yes," he answered. "It is against our rules, sir, to allow any person to take a slave out of Baltimore into Philadelphia unless he can satisfy us that he has a right to take him along."

"Why is that?" asked "Mr. Johnson" innocently.

"Because, sir," the officer answered in a voice and manner that almost chilled the blood of the fugitives, "if we should allow any gentleman to take a slave past here into Philadelphia, and should the gentleman with whom the slave was traveling turn out to be not his rightful owner, and if the real owner should prove that his slave escaped on our railroad, we should have to pay for him."

This conversation attracted the attention of a large number of curious passengers. They seemed sympathetic to "Mr. Johnson," because he was so obviously ill.

Seeing the sympathy of the other passengers, the officer asked, more politely, "Do you know someone in Baltimore who might vouch for you and assure us that you have a right to take this slave into Pennsylvania?"

"No, I do not," asserted "Mr. Johnson" regretfully. He then added more forcefully, "I bought tickets in Charleston to pass us through to Philadelphia, and you have no right to detain us here!"

The officer was firm. "Right or wrong, I shan't let you go."

William and Ellen looked at each other, but did not dare to say a word for fear they would give themselves away. They knew that, if the officer suspected them, he had the right to put them in prison. When their true identity became known, they would surely be sent back into slavery, and they knew they would rather be dead. They silently prayed to be delivered from this new danger.

Just then, the conductor of the train on which they had come from Washington, came in.

"Did this gentleman and his slave come on your train?" asked the official.

"They did," answered the conductor, and left.

Suddenly the bell rang for the train to leave. The other passengers fixed their eyes upon the officer, "Mr. Johnson," and his slave, their expressions showing their interest and concern.

The officer seemed agitated. Running his fingers through his hair, he finally said, "I don't know what to do." Then looking around, he added, "I calculate it is all right. Run and tell the conductor that it will be all right to let this gentleman and his slave proceed," he told one of the clerks. "Since he is not well, it is a pity to stop him here. We will let him go."

"Mr. Johnson" thanked him and stepped out, crossing the platform as quickly as possible, with his slave close behind. William escorted his master into one of the best carriages of the train and reached his own just as the train pulled out.

It was eight o'clock on Christmas Eve, just eight days after William had first thought of their plan. In the four days before they left Macon, he and Ellen had both been working; they had seen each other only at night, when they talked over each detail of their plan. They had had hardly any sleep for the four days of planning and the four days of the journey. Now that the last hurdle was passed, William realized how terribly tired he was. Knowing that they would be in Philadelphia in the morning, and that there were no important stations between Baltimore and Philadelphia, William relaxed his guard, and fell asleep. It proved to be the wrong time for sleeping.

47

When the train reached Havre-de-Grace, all the first-class passengers were told to get off the train and onto a ferryboat, to be ferried across the Susquehanna River to take the train again on the opposite side. This was to spare the passengers the jolting of rolling the cars onto the boat. The baggage cars, however, were rolled on the boat to be taken off on the other side. The sleeping William was near the baggage car, so they did not wake him.

When Ellen left the railroad carriage to get on the ferryboat, it was cold and dark and rainy. She was alone, without William, for the first time on the journey. She was frightened and confused.

"Have you seen my boy?" "Mr. Johnson" asked the conductor.

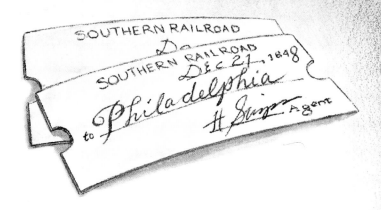

The conductor, who may well have been an abolitionist, thought he would tease this Southern slaveowner.

"No, I haven't seen anything of him for some time; no doubt he has run away and has reached Philadelphia long before now. He is probably a free man by now, sir."

"Mr. Johnson" knew better. "Please try to find him," he asked the conductor.

"I am no slave hunter," the conductor indignantly replied. "As far as I am concerned, everybody must look after his own slaves." With that, he strode away.

Ellen was frightened. She feared that William had been kidnaped into slavery, or perhaps killed on the train. She was in a predicament for another reason. She had no money at all. Although Ellen had been carrying the money up to then, she had given it all to William the night before after hearing that there were pickpockets in Philadelphia who preyed on travelers. A pickpocket would not think of a slave as a likely victim.

Ellen did have the tickets, however. Frightened and confused though she was, she realized that there was no use in her staying there at Havre-de-Grace. She must board the ferry and complete her journey, hoping and praying that she and William would find each other again in freedom.

The ferry ride over, the passengers went back on the train. After the train was well on its way to Philadelphia, the guard came to the car where William was sleeping and gave him a violent shake, saying, "Boy, wake up!"

William started, not knowing for a moment where he was.

"Your master is scared half to death about you," the guard continued. It was William's turn to be scared. He was sure that Ellen had been found out.

"What is the matter?" William managed to ask.

"Your master thinks you have run away from him," the guard explained.

Knowing that Ellen would never think any such thing, William felt reassured and went to his "master" immediately.

After talking with
"Mr. Johnson" for a few minutes,
William returned to his place, where the
guard was talking with the conductor.

"What did your master want, boy?" asked the guard.

"He just wanted to know what had become of me."

"No," said the guard. "That's not it. He thought you
had taken leave for parts unknown. I never saw a man
so badly scared about losing his slave in my life. Now,"
continued the guard, "let me give you a little friendly
advice. When you get to Philadelphia, run away and
leave that cripple, and have your liberty."

"No, sir," replied William. "I can't promise to do that."

"Why not?" asked the conductor, evidently much
surprised. "Don't you want your liberty?"

"Yes, sir," he replied, "but I shall never run away from such a good master as I have at present."

One of the men said to the guard, "Let him alone. I guess he'll open his eyes when he gets to Philadelphia."

In spite of William's seeming lack of interest, the men gave him a good deal of information about how to run away from his master in Philadelphia, information which he appeared not to be taking to heart, but which he found useful for both of them later.

On the train, William also met a free black man, who recommended to him a boardinghouse in Philadelphia kept by an abolitionist, where he would be quite safe if he decided to run away from his master. William thanked him, but did not let him know who he and his "master" really were.

Later on in the night, William heard a fearful whistling of the steam engine; he looked out the window and saw many flickering lights. A passenger in the next car also stuck his head out the window and called to his companion, "Wake up! We are in Philadelphia." The sight of the city in the distance and the words he heard made William feel as if a burden had rolled off his back; he felt really happy for the first time in his life.

As soon as the train reached the platform, he went to get "Mr. Johnson," took their luggage, put it into a carriage, got in and drove off to the abolitionist's boardinghouse recommended to him by the free black man.

No sooner had they left the station than Ellen, who had concealed her fears and played her part with so much courage and wit throughout the journey, grasped William's hand and said, "Thank God we are safe!" She burst into tears, and wept like a child.

When they reached the boardinghouse, Ellen was so weak and faint that she could scarcely stand alone. As soon as they were shown their room, William and Ellen knelt down and thanked God for His goodness in enabling them to overcome so many dangers in escaping from slavery to freedom.

That was Sunday, December 25, Christmas Day of 1848.

Ellen was twenty-two years old, and William a few years older. They thought all their troubles were over. They were young, strong, and in love. And they were free.

Philadelphia was the first stop on the Underground Railroad for William and Ellen. Eventually, they made their way to England, where their children were born. After the Civil War, they returned to Georgia with their family and bought a large plantation. There they established the Woodville Cooperative Farm School for poor families, to which they devoted the rest of their lives.

Meet the Author

Florence B. Freedman

Freedman was born in Brooklyn, New York. She went to school at Columbia University and later became a teacher of English and Hebrew.

Many of Freedman's books are based on stories she heard or read when she was growing up. *Two Tickets to Freedom* is a true story. To write it, Freedman researched old newspaper articles, journals, and William Craft's own narrative of what happened.

Meet the Illustrator

Doris Ettlinger

Ettlinger lives in a three-story, one-hundred-fifty-year-old mill in western New Jersey. Her studio is on the first floor, and she lives on the second floor with her family. On the third floor she teaches an art class. She tells her students to draw every day, even if they are just doodling, because it can help them come up with ideas. She loves to illustrate stories that took place long ago. When working on *Two Tickets to Freedom*, she "enjoyed searching in books and on the Internet for pictures of old trains and costumes from that era."

READING: COMPREHENSION AND ANALYSIS OF GRADE-LEVEL-APPROPRIATE TEXT 2.5 Compare and contrast information on the same topic after reading several passages or articles. READING: STRUCTURAL FEATURES OF LITERATURE 3.2 Identify the main events of the plot, their causes, and the influence of each event on future actions. WRITING: ORGANIZATION AND FOCUS 1.1 Select a focus, an organization structure, and a point of view based upon purpose, audience, length, and format requirements.

CALIFORNIA

Theme Connections

Discuss

Within the Selection

1. What risk do Ellen and William take in the story?

2. What are the possible consequences of that risk?

Across Selections

3. How is the risk that the Crafts take similar to the risk taken by Karana in "Island of the Blue Dolphins"?

4. How are the risks in these two selections different?

Beyond the Selection

5. What people in your community take risks to make things better?

6. What would happen if these people stopped taking risks?

Write

What is important enough to you to make you take a dangerous risk?

Read

To learn more about dangerous risks people have taken throughout history, look for books about the early explorers of California, such as Captain James Cook. Read about the risks explorers took to reach California.

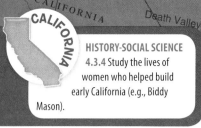

CALIFORNIA

HISTORY-SOCIAL SCIENCE
4.3.4 Study the lives of women who helped build early California (e.g., Biddy Mason).

Social Studies Link

Bridget "Biddy" Mason

Genre

Expository Text tells people something. It contains facts about real people, things, or events.

Text Feature

Charts present information in an organized and visual way.

Did you know that many women were responsible for the early building of California? One of these brave women was Bridget "Biddy" Mason.

Biddy Mason was born a slave on August 15, 1818, in Georgia. In 1847, her master wanted to move to Utah. They traveled through California. Biddy learned that she was in a free state. She asked the court for her freedom and won! Biddy's three daughters and ten other slaves were released from the ownership of others.

As a free woman, Biddy worked as a nurse and midwife. She saved enough money to buy land. She was the first African American to purchase land in Los Angeles. Biddy built a commercial building with rental spaces. This area grew into the central commercial district in the city.

Biddy was sympathetic to the needs of others. She founded a traveler's aid center. The center helped pioneers and immigrants stranded on their journeys. Biddy was a founding member of the First African American Episcopal Church. Her home was often a haven for the homeless. She also delivered food baskets to the jail and cared for the sick. Biddy's kindness earned her the nickname, "Grandma Mason."

Biddy liked to say: "If you hold your hand closed, nothing good can come in. The open hand is blessed, for it gives in abundance, even as it receives." Judging from the goodwill she gave, Biddy's hands were always open.

Think Link

1. How did the trip to California change Biddy's life?

2. Why do you think Biddy was given the nickname "Grandma Mason"?

3. Create a chart with three headings: "Biddy's Action," "People Affected," and "How They Were Affected." Fill in the chart using the information from the article.

WebLink

Visit **www.ImagineItReading. com/AtHome** for more information about Biddy Mason and other famous women who helped build California.

Apply

Charts As you work on your investigation, think about how charts can present information in an organized and visual way.

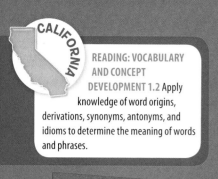

READING: VOCABULARY AND CONCEPT DEVELOPMENT 1.2 Apply knowledge of word origins, derivations, synonyms, antonyms, and idioms to determine the meaning of words and phrases.

Read the story to find the meanings of these words:

- ◆ fluttered
- ◆ recalled
- ◆ authoritative
- ◆ obviously
- ◆ merriment
- ◆ route
- ◆ tangled
- ◆ surge
- ◆ miserable
- ◆ silvery
- ◆ cover
- ◆ circumstances

Vocabulary Development

Word Analysis gives us clues about a word's meaning. The meaning often changes when a prefix or a suffix is added to the root. Use the suffix *-ly* and the root *obvious* to find the meaning of *obviously*.

Vocabulary
Warm-Up

As Nina approached the starting line, her heart fluttered. She recalled her gym teacher's authoritative words from the day before: "Just work together and do your best."

She and Luis were partners for "The Three-Legged Obstacle Race." Their ankles were tied together with rope. This obviously would not be easy.

"On your marks. Get set. Go!" Nina and Luis took off with four other pairs of students. The rest of their classmates cheered in merriment.

Their route would take them across the entire gym floor, around cones, and over small hurdles. They would dribble basketballs, ride scooters, and dodge water balloons.

Less than ten seconds into the race, one of the other pairs got tangled up and tumbled to the floor. They were not hurt, just embarrassed.

Nina and Luis made it through the cones without falling, but the hurdles were harder.

"Ouch!" Luis cried, as they barely cleared the first hurdle.

"What's wrong?" asked Nina, as she felt a surge in the rope tying her to Luis.

"Our rope is tied too tightly," he replied.

"We're more than halfway finished," Nina told him. "You're not too miserable, are you?"

"I'm okay," Luis said, as they picked up two basketballs and began to dribble them.

The last stretch was the water balloon dodge. Their classmates were armed and ready on the sidelines.

Nina and Luis ran and ducked as the first few balloons flew by. One silvery balloon came straight for Nina's head. She put up her hand for cover, but Luis swatted it away.

"That was close," said Nina, laughing as they crossed the finish line immediately after the first-place duo.

"We're still a little wet," Luis said, "but under the circumstances, I'd say we make a great team!"

Vocabulary Word Web

Take turns writing and responding to *yes* or *no* questions using the vocabulary words. You might ask, "Is it fun to be *miserable?*" Your partner should circle the correct answer and write a reason in the second box.

Concept Vocabulary

This lesson's concept word is **conscience.** *Conscience* means "a sense of right and wrong." You might have heard someone say, "Let your conscience be your guide." What do you think that phrase means? When a friend asks you to do something that you are not sure is okay, how can your conscience help you make the right decision?

CALIFORNIA

READING: STRUCTURAL
FEATURES OF LITERATURE
3.1 Describe the structural
differences of various forms
of literature, including fantasies, fables,
myths, legends, and fairy tales. READING:
NARRATIVE ANALYSIS OF GRADE-LEVEL-
APPROPRIATE TEXT 3.2 Identify the main
events of the plot, their causes, and the
influence of each event on future actions.
3.3 Use knowledge of the situation and
setting and of a character's traits and
motivations to determine the causes for
that character's actions.

Genre

A **fantasy** is an imaginary story that contains characters, settings, or events that are impossible and do not exist in the real world.

Comprehension Skill

☆ **Cause and Effect** Identifying cause-and-effect relationships as you read will help you understand the connections among events in the selection.

Mrs. Frisby and the Crow

by Robert C. O'Brien

illustrated by John Kanzler

Focus Questions

Are there times when we must take a risk to help others? Can our own risks sometimes endanger others?

Mrs. Frisby is a mouse that lives with her children in a country garden. When her son Timothy becomes ill, she undertakes a treacherous journey to bring him some medicine.

Mrs. Frisby looked again at the sun and saw that she faced an unpleasant choice. She could go home by the same roundabout way she had come, in which case she would surely end up walking alone in the woods in the dark—a frightening prospect, for at night the forest was alive with danger. Then the owl came out to hunt, and foxes, weasels and strange wild cats stalked among the tree trunks.

The other choice would be dangerous, too, but with luck it would get her home before dark. That would be to take a straighter route, across the farmyard between the barn and the chicken house, going not too close to the house but cutting the distance home by half. The cat would be there somewhere, but by daylight—and by staying in the open, away from the shrubs—she could probably spot him before he saw her.

The cat: He was called Dragon. Farmer Fitzgibbon's wife had given him the name as a joke when he was a small kitten pretending to be fierce. But when he grew up, the name turned out to be an apt one. He was enormous, with a huge, broad head and a large mouth full of curving fangs, needle sharp. He had seven claws on each foot and a thick, furry tail, which lashed angrily from side to side. In color he was orange and white, with glaring yellow eyes; and when he leaped to kill, he gave a high, strangled scream that froze his victims where they stood.

But Mrs. Frisby preferred not to think about that. Instead, as she came out of the woods from Mr. Ages' house and reached the farmyard fence she thought about Timothy. She thought of how his eyes shone with merriment when he made up small jokes, which he did frequently, and how invariably kind he was to his small, scatterbrained sister Cynthia. The other children sometimes laughed at her when she made mistakes, or grew impatient with her because she was forever losing things; but Timothy never did. Instead, he would help her find them. And when Cynthia herself had been sick in bed with a cold, he had sat by her side for hours and entertained her with stories. He made these up out of his head, and he seemed to have a bottomless supply of them.

Taking a firm grip on her packets of medicine, Mrs. Frisby went under the fence and set out toward the farmyard. The first stretch was a long pasture; the barn itself, square and red and big, rose in the distance to her right; to her left, farther off, were the chicken houses.

When at length she came abreast of the barn, she
saw the cattle wire fence that marked the other end of the
pasture; and as she approached it, she was startled by a
sudden outburst of noise. She thought at first it was a hen,
strayed from the chicken yard—caught by a fox? She looked
down the fence and saw that it was no hen at all, but a
young crow, flapping in the grass, acting most odd. As she
watched, he fluttered to the top wire of the fence, where
he perched nervously for a moment. Then he spread his
wings, flapped hard, and took off—but after flying four feet
he stopped with a snap and crashed to the ground again,
shedding a flurry of black feathers and squawking loudly.

He was tied to the fence. A piece of something silvery—it looked like wire—was tangled around one of his legs; the other end of it was caught in the fence. Mrs. Frisby walked closer, and then she could see it was not wire after all, but a length of silver-colored string, probably left over from a Christmas package.

The crow was sitting on the fence, pecking ineffectively at the string with his bill, cawing softly to himself, a miserable sound. After a moment he spread his wings, and she could see he was going to try to fly again.

"Wait," said Mrs. Frisby.

The crow looked down and saw her in the grass.

"Why should I wait? Can't you see I'm caught? I've got to get loose."

"But if you make so much noise again the cat is sure to hear. If he hasn't heard already."

"You'd make noise, too, if you were tied to a fence with a piece of string, and with night coming on."

"I would not," said Mrs. Frisby, "if I had any sense and knew there was a cat nearby. Who tied you?" She was trying to calm the crow, who was obviously terrified.

He looked embarrassed and stared at his feet. "I picked up the string. It got tangled with my foot. I sat on the fence to try to get it off, and it caught on the fence."

"*Why* did you pick up the string?"

The crow, who was very young indeed—in fact, only a year old—said wearily, "Because it was shiny."

"You knew better."

"I had been told."

Birdbrain, thought Mrs. Frisby, and then recalled what her husband used to say: The size of the brain is no measure of its capacity. And well she might recall it, for the crow's head was double the size of her own.

"Sit quietly," she said. "Look toward the house and see if you see the cat."

"I don't see him. But I can't see behind the bushes. Oh, if I could just fly higher . . ."

"Don't," said Mrs. Frisby. She looked at the sun; it was setting behind the trees. She thought of Timothy, and of the medicine she was carrying. Yet she knew she could not leave the foolish crow there to be killed—and killed he surely would be before sunrise—just for want of a few minutes' work. She might still make it by dusk if she hurried.

"Come down here," she said. "I'll get the string off."

"How?" said the crow dubiously.

"Don't argue. I have only a few minutes." She said this in a voice so authoritative that the crow fluttered down immediately.

"But if the cat comes . . ." he said.

"If the cat comes, he'll knock you off the fence with one jump and catch you with the next. Be still." She was already at work with her sharp teeth, gnawing at the string. It was twined and twisted and twined again around his right ankle, and she saw she would have to cut through it three times to get it off.

As she finished the second strand, the crow, who was staring toward the house, suddenly cried out:

"I see the cat!"

"*Quiet!*" whispered Mrs. Frisby. "Does he see us?"

"I don't know. Yes. He's looking at me. I don't think he can see you."

"Stand perfectly still. Don't get in a panic." She did not look up, but started on the third strand.

"He's moving this way."

"Fast or slow?"

"Medium. I think he's trying to figure out what I'm doing."

She cut through the last strand,
gave a tug, and the string fell off.

"There, you're free. Fly off, and be quick."

"But what about you?"

"Maybe he hasn't seen me."

"But he will. He's coming closer."

Mrs. Frisby looked around. There was not a bit of cover
anywhere near, not a rock nor a hole nor a log; nothing
at all closer than the chicken yard—and that was in the
direction the cat was coming from, and a long way off.

"Look," said the crow. "Climb on my back. Quick. And
hang on."

Mrs. Frisby did what she was told, first grasping the
precious packages of medicine tightly between her teeth.

"Are you on?"

"Yes."

She gripped the feathers on his back, felt the beat of his powerful black wings, felt a dizzying upward surge, and shut her eyes tight.

"Just in time," said the crow, and she heard the angry scream of the cat as he leaped at where they had just been. "It's lucky you're so light. I can scarcely tell you're there." Lucky indeed, thought Mrs. Frisby; if it had not been for your foolishness, I'd never have gotten into such a scrape. However, she thought it wise not to say so, under the circumstances.

"Where do you live?" asked the crow.

"In the garden patch. Near the big stone."

"I'll drop you off there." He banked alarmingly, and for a moment Mrs. Frisby thought he meant it literally. But a few seconds later—so fast does the crow fly— they were gliding to earth a yard from her front door.

"Thank you very much," said Mrs. Frisby, hopping to the ground.

"It's I who should be thanking you," said the crow. "You saved my life."

"And you mine."

"Ah, but that's not quite even. Yours wouldn't have been risked if it had not been for me—me and my piece of string." And since this was just what she had been thinking, Mrs. Frisby did not argue.

"We all help one another against the cat," she said.

"True. Just the same, I am in debt to you. If the time ever comes when I can help you, I hope you will ask me. My name is Jeremy. Mention it to any crow you see in these woods, and he will find me."

"Thank you," said Mrs. Frisby. "I will remember."

Jeremy flew away to the woods, and she entered her house, taking the three doses of medicine with her.

Robert C. O'Brien

O'Brien could sing before he could talk. His favorite toy was the family's wind-up Victrola (music player). He learned to play piano when he was very young, and he stayed with it all his life.

His other favorite thing to do was create splendid imaginary worlds, with himself in dazzling, heroic roles. In his forties he decided to share those worlds with others, so he started writing books.

"When I get a story idea," he said, "I write it down before I forget it. It isn't always for children, but those are the stories I most like to write."

Meet the Illustrator

John Kanzler

Kanzler has been drawing since he can remember. His parents' support helped him become a professional artist. Kanzler says, "I never felt discouraged, since I was doing what I loved." He loves to draw animals the most. He lives on a small farm and has one bird, two llamas, four sheep, and five cats.

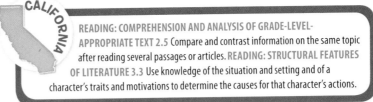

READING: COMPREHENSION AND ANALYSIS OF GRADE-LEVEL-APPROPRIATE TEXT 2.5 Compare and contrast information on the same topic after reading several passages or articles. READING: STRUCTURAL FEATURES OF LITERATURE 3.3 Use knowledge of the situation and setting and of a character's traits and motivations to determine the causes for that character's actions.

Theme Connections

Discuss

Within the Selection

1. Why does Mrs. Frisby risk her life to remove the string from Jeremy's leg?

2. What risk does Jeremy take to save Mrs. Frisby's life?

Across Selections

3. How do the risks that Mrs. Frisby takes compare to those taken by Karana in "Island of the Blue Dolphins" and the Crafts in "Two Tickets to Freedom"?

4. Which of the characters in the selections you have read so far do you think take the biggest risks? Why?

Beyond the Selection

5. Why do people take life-threatening risks?

6. What would make you take a life-threatening risk?

Write

Describe a time you decided *not* to take a risk.

Read

Find magazines that deal with a risky sport, hobby, or pastime. Ask yourself if you would take the same risks to do something you loved.

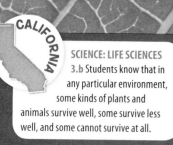

CALIFORNIA
SCIENCE: LIFE SCIENCES
3.b Students know that in any particular environment, some kinds of plants and animals survive well, some survive less well, and some cannot survive at all.

Science Link

Amazing Animals

Genre

Expository Text tells people something. It contains facts about real people, things, or events.

Text Feature

Headings tell readers what a paragraph is going to be about.

Animals can change their behavior to survive. We call this type of change an adaptive trait. Some of these behaviors might seem strange. But animals do these things for a good reason. They are fighting to stay alive!

Finding Food

Squirrels gather acorns and nuts before winter and store them. When winter arrives, the squirrels are well fed. A chimpanzee pokes a stick into a termite mound. Then he pulls it out. It is covered with termites. He licks them off and eats them.

Surviving Harsh Weather

A hippopotamus takes mud baths to survive hot weather. The mud keeps the hippo's skin wet so it will not dry and crack. The mud also keeps insects from gnawing its skin. Some birds travel to warmer places when winter comes. Other animals take a similar route. This is called migration. Some animals hibernate. They spend the winter in a deep sleep.

Avoiding Enemies

Opossums are good at playing dead. This keeps them from being eaten. Skunks give off a smelly spray. This keeps predators away. The spray is called musk. An octopus can change its skin color. This helps it hide from enemies.

Think Link

1. When porcupines feel threatened, they roll into a ball with only their spiny quills sticking out. Under which heading in the selection would the porcupine fit?

2. What is the difference between migration and hibernation?

3. What other adaptive animal traits can you think of?

CALIFORNIA WebLink

Visit **www.ImagineItReading.com/ AtHome** for more information about the survival strategies of animals.

Apply

Headings As you work on your investigation, think about how you can use headings to help organize your ideas.

CALIFORNIA

READING: VOCABULARY AND CONCEPT DEVELOPMENT 1.2 Apply knowledge of word origins, derivations, synonyms, antonyms, and idioms to determine the meaning of words and phrases.

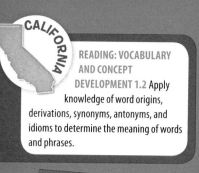

Read the story to find the meanings of these words, which are also in "Langston Hughes: Poet of the People":

- ✦ concerned
- ✦ glumly
- ✦ decent
- ✦ success
- ✦ preoccupied
- ✦ biology
- ✦ crumpled
- ✦ strive
- ✦ tensely
- ✦ stubborn
- ✦ opportunities
- ✦ practical

Vocabulary Development

Word Analysis gives us clues about a word's meaning. The meaning often changes when a prefix or a suffix is added to a root word. Look at the word *concerned*.

Vocabulary
Warm-Up

"I'm really concerned about our new business," Miguel said glumly.

"What do you mean?" asked Jamar, puzzled. "We have been bringing in a decent amount of money, haven't we?

"Yes, the business has been a success so far," Miguel admitted. "It is the future I am worried about."

"You've lost me, buddy," said Jamar, preoccupied with his biology textbook.

"When we started Wash-n-Walk six months ago, lots of people wanted us to groom and exercise their dogs," said Miguel. His face crumpled with worry. "We had to strive to keep all our customers happy. Now it seems like we are pleading with people for business."

Jamar laughed.

"What's so funny?" Miguel asked tensely.

"I'm sorry," Jamar said smiling. "You just remind me of my dad. He always paces back and forth when he is being stubborn. But I will tell you what is happening. We started our business late in the fall. The setting was perfect. People were too busy to wash their dogs, or it was too cold for them to go outside and walk them. Now summer is on the way. People want to be outside. But in six months, we will be back in business!"

"That makes sense," Miguel said. "But what are we going to do in the meantime?"

"Well, we can take the summer off," Jamar said, "or we can think of other business opportunities for the warmer months."

"How about a lemonade stand?" Miguel suggested.

"Keep thinking of practical ideas, buddy!" Jamar laughed.

Vocabulary Word Play

On a separate sheet of paper, work with a partner to create a short paragraph using the vocabulary words. Then share your paragraph with the class.

Concept Vocabulary

This lesson's concept word is **consider**. *Consider* means "to think carefully about something before deciding." There are many situations in life where it is best to consider your options before making a decision. One is spending a lot of money on a certain item. What other situations can you think of where it is important to take time for consideration?

CALIFORNIA

READING: COMPREHENSION AND ANALYSIS OF GRADE-LEVEL-APPROPRIATE TEXT

2.2 Use appropriate strategies when reading for different purposes (e.g., full comprehension, location of information, personal enjoyment).

Genre

A **play** is a story that is written to be performed by actors before an audience. The writer, or playwright, tells the story chiefly through the dialogue of the characters.

Comprehension Skill

Author's Purpose
As you read, identify the reason, or purpose, the author has for writing the text. This skill will give you an idea of what to expect from the selection.

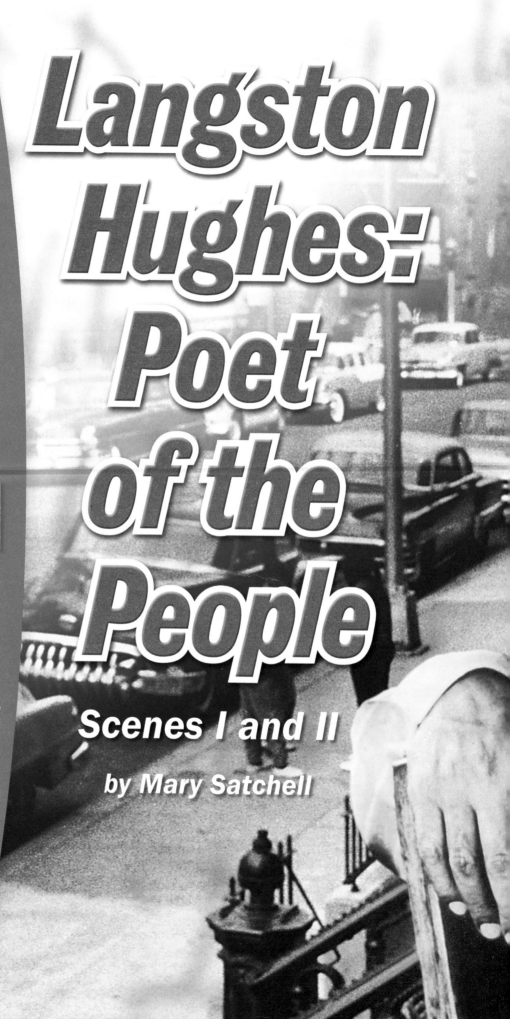

Langston Hughes: Poet of the People

Scenes I and II

by Mary Satchell

Focus Questions

What might prevent you from taking a risk? What would the world be like if no one ever took a risk?

CHARACTERS

Langston Hughes, *Black American writer*

Mr. James Hughes, *his father*

Señora Garcia, *housekeeper*

Thad, *medical student*

Scene 1

TIME:

Summer, 1920.

SETTING:

Study in James Hughes's home near Mexico City. A desk, chair, and wastebasket are center. Accountant's ledger lies closed on edge of desk. Floor vase with tall pampas grass is nearby.

AT RISE:

Langston Hughes sits writing at desk. Señora Garcia enters, holding feather duster.

Señora Garcia:

Señor Langston, how can you sit in one place for hours just writing?

Langston *(Leaning back)*:

Señora Garcia, if I could spend my whole life writing, I'd be happy.

Señora Garcia *(Dusting vase)*:

> You are a true artist, Señor Langston. *(Turns; sighs)* It is too bad that your father does not understand. You two belong to different worlds. You are a dreamer, and he is such a practical man.

Langston *(Thoughtfully)*:

> Father and I still don't know each other very well. *(Rises)* Since I arrived, he's been trying to make me into what *he* thinks I should be.

Señora Garcia *(Putting hands on hips)*:

> I have been your father's housekeeper for a long time. Señor Hughes is a very stubborn man. But I'm sure he wants the best for you because you are *hijo querido*—his only son. *(Door slams off.* Langston *and* Señora Garcia *turn.)*

Langston *(Tensely)*:

> That must be Father, and I haven't finished those accounting problems he left for me.

Señora Garcia *(Giving ledger to* Langston*)*:

> Quickly, Señor Langston! Take this ledger and give me those papers you've been writing on before your father sees them. He will be angry to find you have been writing poems. *(She sweeps papers into desk drawer, but one falls unnoticed to the floor.)*

Langston *(Earnestly)*:

> But, Señora Garcia, I can't be a make-believe son for my father any longer.

Señora Garcia (*Pushing* Langston *into chair*):
Señor Langston, if you don't do as I say, you had better brace yourself for a thunderstorm. (Mr. Hughes *enters, frowning.* Señora Garcia *turns with big smile.*) *Buenas dias,* Señor Hughes. We were not expecting you back from Toluca so soon.

Mr. Hughes:
Hello, Señora Garcia. (*As he removes his poncho*) Langston?

Langston (*Rising; uncomfortable*):
Hello, Father. (Mr. Hughes *gives poncho to* Señora Garcia, *who exits with it.*)

Mr. Hughes:
Well, Langston, let me see what progress you've made with the accounting problems.

Langston (*Hesitantly*):
Father, I need to talk to you.

Mr. Hughes (*Pointing to ledger*):
We should go over the accounting problems first, and after dinner, we'll work on your Spanish lessons.

Langston (*Pleading*):
Father, please listen to me. . .

Mr. Hughes:
We can talk later, son. Let me see your bookkeeping. If you're going to run this ranch someday, you'll have to learn how to keep accounts. (*Sits at desk*)

Langston (*Giving ledger to Mr. Hughes*):
I'm afraid I didn't get much done.

Mr. Hughes *(Slowly turning pages; irritated)*:

Langston, you've hardly done any work on these at all.

Langston *(Pleading)*:

I tried—I really did. *(Sighs)* Accounting just isn't for me.
I'm more interested in other things *(Paces)*—like writing.

Mr. Hughes *(Slamming ledger shut)*:

So—just as I thought. I suppose you've been sitting
around here since I left—daydreaming?

Langston:

Actually, I've been very busy.

Mr. Hughes *(Angrily)*:

I didn't bring you to Mexico just to waste your life, Langston.

Langston:

I appreciate what you're doing for me, but—

Mr. Hughes *(Banging desk)*:

No excuses! You can be as successful as I am. *(Rises)*
I left the States and moved here to Mexico because here
a black man can live like any other man. That's why
I insisted you move here from Cleveland . . . so you can
have more opportunities! Here if he works hard, a man
can be a success at whatever he wants.

Langston *(Confidently)*:

I plan to be a successful writer.

Mr. Hughes:

Nonsense! You'll attend a good school and earn a degree
in engineering.

Langston *(Surprised)*:

Engineering?

Mr. Hughes:

Of course. *(Proudly)* I can afford to send you to the finest schools in the world. *(Thoughtfully)* I hear there are excellent schools in Switzerland.

Langston *(Stunned)*:

Switzerland! *(Agitated)* I don't want to go to school halfway around the world.

Mr. Hughes:

All right, if you feel that strongly about it. Let's see. *(Thinks)* What are some schools with good engineering departments?

Langston *(Eagerly)*:

What about Columbia?

Mr. Hughes:

Columbia University in New York City?

Langston:

Yes. My grades were good in high school. I think Columbia would accept me.

Mr. Hughes *(Pleased)*:

That's more like it. Now, forget that silly writing business, and we'll see about getting you an application for Columbia. (Señora Garcia *enters*.)

Señora Garcia:

Excuse me. Dinner is ready, Señor.

Mr. Hughes:

We'll be right there. *(He turns, sees paper on floor.)* What's this?

Langston *(Hurriedly)*:

It's nothing. I'll get it. (Mr. Hughes *picks up paper, glances at it, and frowns.*)

Mr. Hughes:

Is this one of your poems?

Langston *(Sheepishly)*:

Yes. *(Reaches for paper, but* Mr. Hughes *crumples it.)*

Mr. Hughes *(Sternly)*:

You won't have any more time for poetry. *(Drops paper into wastebasket and puts arm around* Langston's *shoulders)* We'll talk later about what courses you'll take at Columbia University next year. You'll have to study a lot of science and math. *(They exit.* Señora Garcia *takes crumpled paper from wastebasket, smooths it out.)*

Señora Garcia *(Sadly)*:

Poor Señor Langston. Why can't his father just accept him the way he is? *(Puts paper in desk drawer and exits. Curtain)*

Scene 2

TIME:

The next year.

SETTING:

Langston's dormitory room at Columbia University. Bunk or twin beds and small bureau are upstage. Desk with papers, pencils, and books; two chairs; lamp, clock, and wastebasket are downstage. Closet door is in wall right. Exit is left. Large posters of Harlem street and café scenes are on wall upstage.

AT RISE:

Thad *sits at desk, reading.* Langston *enters.*

Langston:

Hi, Thad. I don't suppose my father has shown up yet.

Thad:

No, he hasn't, Lang, but if I were you, I'd get out of town before he arrives.

Langston *(With a forced laugh)*:

You talk as if you've already met him. *(Sighs)* He's probably very angry with me now.

Thad:

Can't say I blame him. *(Closes book)* Lang, what gives with you? All you've been doing lately is skipping classes and spending all your time uptown in Harlem. You haven't touched a book in weeks.

Langston *(Placing jacket on chair)*:

I've tried to stick to my studies, Thad, but—*(Sighs)* my heart's just not in engineering.

Thad *(Rising)*:

Do you think I enjoy studying all the time? Sometimes I'd like to forget this *(Points to book)* and go uptown with you. *(Pauses; glances at posters)* It sure would be great to dig some jazz and just unwind for a while. (*He moves back to desk.*) But I want to earn a decent living someday. A medical degree is my ticket to a good life.

Langston:

I always thought you really wanted to be a doctor.

Thad:

I *do* want to be a doctor.

Langston:

But you just said that a medical degree is a *ticket* to somewhere.

Thad *(Defensively)*:

It's a ticket to a comfortable home, a fine car, and all the other things I want in life.

Langston *(Disappointed)*:

I thought a man decided to become a doctor in order to help people.

Thad *(Shrugging)*:

You're too idealistic, Lang.

Langston *(Thoughtfully)*:

Maybe a better word would be *honest*. And speaking of honesty, I've decided it's time to tell my father the truth.

Thad:

What are you going to tell him?

Langston *(Earnestly)*:

That I just don't want to be an engineer. I came here to be near the Harlem scene, but I'm studying engineering only to please him.

Thad *(Putting hand on* Langston's *shoulder)*:

You've got to be practical, Lang. An engineering career makes sense.

Langston:

For me, everything has to come from the heart, or it's nothing. I want to write poems, stories, and plays about black Americans. Harlem's where I belong.

Thad *(Incredulously)*:

You'd give up a stable future to spend your time in Harlem?

Hughes and friends at the Booker T. Washington statue

Langston:

Yes.

Thad (*Concerned*):

But if you make a foolish decision now. . .

Langston (*Passionately*):

At least I'll know I've been true to myself.

Thad (*Embarrassed; looking at clock*):

I have a biology class soon. Your father will be here any minute.

Langston (*Glumly; sitting*):

I guess I'd better brace myself for a storm. (Thad *gets jacket from closet and picks up book.*)

Thad (*Trying to be cheerful*):

Don't look so down, Lang. Once you're into your engineering courses, we'll both laugh about the way you feel now.

Langston:

I don't think so. (Thad *exits.* Langston *picks up pencil and writes. Knocking is heard offstage.* Langston, *preoccupied, does not answer. After a moment,* Mr. Hughes *enters.*)

Mr. Hughes (*Frowning*):

Langston. (Langston *looks up.*) I hope you were too deep in your studies to hear my knocking.

Langston (*Rising*):

Hello, Father. (*Uncomfortably*) I know you're here because of my grades.

Mr. Hughes:

I don't have to tell you how disappointed I am. (*Sits*)

Langston *(Sighing)*:

It's time for me to be honest with you. When I came to Columbia, I tried to convince myself that it was to earn a degree, but I really wanted to get to Harlem.

Mr. Hughes *(Bewildered)*:

What's Harlem got to do with this?

Langston:

Everything. Thousands of black Americans live in Harlem, and I want to live with them. I have a burning desire to write about black people—our joys, sorrows . . . everything.

Mr. Hughes *(Irritably; rising)*:

Langston, are you telling me you want to drop out of Columbia?

Langston *(Calmly)*:

Yes. Writing is the only future for me.

Mr. Hughes *(Angrily)*:

If you quit school, you won't get another red cent from me.

Langston:

It's not your money I need now, Father.

Mr. Hughes *(Softening)*:

Langston, I know I could never make up for all those years when you and your mother lived without me. But I tried to give you this opportunity—a ticket to success. (Langston *shakes his head sadly.*)

Langston:

I have to strive for success in my own way.

Mr. Hughes:

Is that your final decision?

Langston *(Quietly)*:

Yes, it is.

Mr. Hughes:

Then I won't argue with you anymore. *(Puts on hat)* I'm returning to Mexico City on the morning train. *(Turns to exit)*

Langston:

Is that all you're going to say?

Mr. Hughes *(Turning back; sadly)*:

I wish you well, Langston, but I feel you're making a foolish mistake. I honestly have my doubts that you'll ever become a successful writer. *(Exits. Langston moves to closet, takes out suitcase, puts it on bed. He moves to bureau and starts packing. Lights slowly fade. Curtain.)*

Langston Hughes played an important role in the Harlem Renaissance of the 1920s and early 1930s. This movement, led by African American artists, musicians, and writers, aimed for racial equality and minority rights. Today, Hughes is recognized as one of America's finest poets.

Langston Hughes withdrew from Columbia University after his first year of classes. He later enrolled in Pennsylvania's Lincoln University, graduating in 1929.

Meet the Author

Mary Satchell

As a college student, Satchell marched with Dr. Martin Luther King Jr. to protest racial discrimination. When she became a teacher, she wanted to use plays to teach her students about famous African Americans and Hispanics. Few plays had been written about them, so Satchell wrote her own. Since retiring from teaching, Satchell has been able to write plays full time. Satchell says of her career, "What joy! My life couldn't be better."

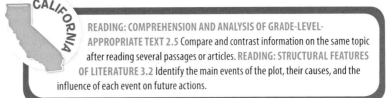

READING: COMPREHENSION AND ANALYSIS OF GRADE-LEVEL-APPROPRIATE TEXT 2.5 Compare and contrast information on the same topic after reading several passages or articles. READING: STRUCTURAL FEATURES OF LITERATURE 3.2 Identify the main events of the plot, their causes, and the influence of each event on future actions.

Theme Connections

Discuss

Within the Selection

1. What risk does Langston Hughes take in the play?

2. Do you think Hughes was right to go against his father's wishes to pursue his dream?

Across Selections

3. How is the risk Hughes takes different from that taken by Karana in "Island of the Blue Dolphins"?

4. How is the risk Hughes takes similar to that taken by the Crafts in "Two Tickets to Freedom"?

Beyond the Selection

5. What does "Langston Hughes: Poet of the People" tell you about why people take risks?

6. Name some other risks that do not involve physical danger.

Write

Describe a time you decided to risk someone's disapproval. What was the result?

Read

Find magazine or newspaper articles that discuss the consequences—good or bad—of a risk someone took.

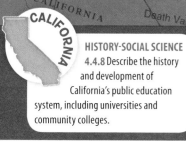

CALIFORNIA

HISTORY-SOCIAL SCIENCE
4.4.8 Describe the history
and development of
California's public education
system, including universities
and community colleges.

Social Studies Link

Public Schools

Genre

An **interview** is a conversation conducted by a reporter to gather facts from someone.

Text Feature

A **line graph** is a diagram, or drawing, of lines that are connected to show how numbers have changed over time.

Kara: This is Kara Carter of KØØ7. We are reporting live from sunny San Francisco. This week we are talking about public schools in California. Chinh, a local fourth grader, has agreed to help us out. Good morning, Chinh. What can you tell us about public schools?

Chinh: Well, in 1849, John C. Pelton and his wife came here from Boston. They started a school in an old Baptist church in San Francisco. It had only three students! At first, only poor students could attend for free. Then in 1850, the city made it the first free public school in California. Soon, every child had opportunities for education.

Kara: Wow, Chinh, I am impressed. You sure know a decent amount of history. What else?

Chinh: Back then, students went to school from 8:30 A.M. until noon and then from 2 to 5 P.M.

Kara: What do you know about schools today?

Chinh: The best thing is how diverse they are. My family came here from Vietnam six years ago. I have students in my class from five other countries. Our state borders Mexico, so many students speak Spanish. We need a lot of teachers and a lot of books.

Kara: Six million students attend public schools in California today. We have come a long way.

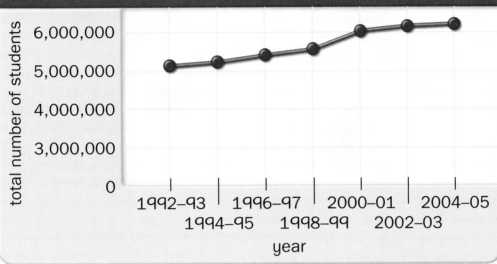

Students Enrolled in California Public Schools from 1992–2005

total number of students

6,000,000

5,000,000

4,000,000

3,000,000

0

1992–93   1996–97   2000–01   2004–05
    1994–95   1998–99   2002–03

year

1. Based on the line graph, how many students do you think will be enrolled in California public schools in the year 2015? Give evidence to support your answer.

2. Why do so many students in California speak Spanish?

3. California is the most ethnically diverse state in America. Why do you think this is?

WebLink

CALIFORNIA

Visit **www.ImagineItReading.com/ AtHome** for more information about the history of public education in California.

Apply

Graphs As you work on your investigation, think about how a graph could help illustrate your ideas.

CALIFORNIA

READING: VOCABULARY
AND CONCEPT
DEVELOPMENT 1.2 Apply
knowledge of word origins,
derivations, synonyms, antonyms, and
idioms to determine the meaning of
words and phrases. 1.3 Use knowledge of
root words to determine the meaning of
unknown words within a passage.

Read the story to find the meanings of these words, which are also in "Daedalus and Icarus":

+ courtyards
+ history
+ jeered
+ brilliant
+ luxurious
+ island
+ plume
+ astonishment
+ shrill
+ nudged
+ drooping
+ crowed

Vocabulary Development

Context Clues are hints in the text that help you find the meanings of words. Define *nudged* and *crowed* by context clues.

Vocabulary

Warm-Up

Jasmine squeezed her Aunt Cheri's hand as they walked up the hill to a big, open field. Every July, Jasmine and Cheri, left their home in the city, and spent a glorious week in the country. Cheri had friends who lived on a 100-acre farm with wide courtyards. The land had a great deal of history to it.

Each night, the two of them would take two blankets, a pair of binoculars, and a container of lemonade out to the field. They would watch the stars for two or three hours at a time. Jasmine loved stargazing, though her friends back home jeered at the idea. She could do it forever. She still could not get over how brilliant the stars looked when they left the city.

They found the perfect spot and spread out their soft, luxurious blankets. They pretended that they were on their own island. Oh, how nice it was to sit in the open air! There wasn't a plume of clouds in the sky.

Cheri always let Jasmine use the binoculars first. As she put them up to her eyes, she gasped with astonishment. "There must be millions of stars up there!" she squealed in a shrill voice.

"You say that every time," Cheri laughed.

Just then, Cheri nudged Jasmine with her elbow. "Jaz, look!" she cried, "a falling star!"

Jasmine looked where Cheri was pointing. Sure enough, a single bright star plunged from its place in the sky. They watched its tail drooping toward the horizon.

"Falling stars are my favorite!" Jasmine crowed with delight.

"I think you will be an astronomer someday," Cheri said with a smile.

"That would be a dream come true," Jasmine replied.

Vocabulary Word Play

Work with a partner to create similes, using *like* or *as*, with the vocabulary words. Share your similes with the rest of the class.

Concept Vocabulary

The concept word for this lesson is *judgment. Judgment* means "an opinion or conclusion reached through reasoning." Give an example of a time when you or someone you know used bad judgment. What would have been a better decision?

CALIFORNIA

READING: COMPREHENSION AND ANALYSIS OF GRADE-LEVEL-APPROPRIATE TEXT
2.3 Make and confirm predictions about text by using prior knowledge and ideas presented in the text itself, including illustrations, titles, topic sentences, important words, and foreshadowing clues. READING: STRUCTURAL FEATURES OF LITERATURE 3.1 Describe the structural differences of various forms of literature, including fantasies, fables, myths, legends, and fairy tales.

Genre

A **myth** tells how something in nature came to be the way it is, or explains why people act certain ways. Often myths contain a lesson about bad behavior.

Comprehension Strategy

Predicting
As you read, make predictions about what you think will happen later in the text. Then check to see whether your predictions are confirmed.

Daedalus and Icarus

retold by Geraldine McCaughrean

illustrated by Emma Chichester Clark

Focus Questions

Do we always recognize when we are taking a risk? Why do people take foolish risks?

Daedalus and Icarus lived in great comfort in King Minos's palace. But they lived the life of prisoners. Their rooms were in the tallest palace tower, with beautiful views across the island. They ate delectable food and wore expensive clothes. But at night the door to their fine apartment was locked, and a guard stood outside. It was a comfortable prison, but it was a prison, even so. Daedalus was deeply unhappy.

Every day he put seed out on the windowsill, for the birds. He liked to study their brilliant colors, the clever overlapping of their feathers, the way they soared on the sea wind. It comforted him to think that they at least were free to come and go. The birds had only to spread their wings and they could leave Crete behind them, whereas Daedalus and Icarus must stay forever in their luxurious cage.

Young Icarus could not understand his father's unhappiness. "But I like it here," he said. "The king gives us gold and this tall tower to live in."

Daedalus groaned. "But to work for such a wicked man, Icarus! And to be prisoners all our days! . . . We shan't stay. We shan't!"

"But we can't get away, can we?" said Icarus. "How can anybody escape from an island? Fly?" He snorted with laughter.

Daedalus did not answer. He scratched his head and stared out of the window at the birds pecking seed on the sill.

From that day onward, he got up early each morning and stood at the open window. When a bird came for the seed, Daedalus begged it to spare him one feather. Then each night, when everyone else had gone to bed, Daedalus worked by candlelight on his greatest invention of all.

Early mornings. Late nights. A whole year went by. Then one morning Icarus was awakened by his father shaking his shoulder. "Get up, Icarus, and don't make a sound. We are leaving Crete."

"But how? It's impossible!"

Daedalus pulled out a bundle from under his bed. "I've been making something, Icarus." Inside were four great folded fans of feathers. He stretched them out on the bed. They were wings! "I sewed the feathers together with strands of wool from my blanket. Now hold still."

Daedalus melted down a candle and daubed his son's shoulders with sticky wax. "Yes, I know it's hot, but it will soon cool." While the wax was still soft, he stuck the wings to Icarus's shoulder blades.

"Now you must help me put on my wings, Son. When the wax sets hard, you and I will fly away from here, as free as birds!"

"I'm scared!" whispered Icarus as he stood on the narrow window ledge, his knees knocking and his huge wings drooping down behind. The lawns and courtyards of the palace lay far below. The royal guards looked as small as ants. "This won't work!"

"Courage, Son!" said Daedalus. "Keep your arms out wide and fly close to me. Above all—are you listening, Icarus?"

"Y-y-yes, father."

"Above all, don't fly too high! Don't fly too close to the sun!"

"Don't fly too close to the sun," Icarus repeated, with his eyes tight shut. Then he gave a cry as his father nudged him off the windowsill.

He plunged downward. With a crack, the feathers behind him filled with wind, and Icarus found himself flying. Flying!

"I'm flying!" he crowed.

The guards looked up in astonishment, and wagged their swords, and pointed and shouted, "Tell the king! Daedalus and Icarus are . . . are . . . flying away!"

By dipping first one wing, then the other, Icarus found that he could turn to the left and the right. The wind tugged at his hair. His legs trailed out behind him. He saw the fields and streams as he had never seen them before!

Then they were out over the sea. The sea gulls pecked at him angrily, so Icarus flew higher, where they could not reach him.

He copied their shrill cry and taunted them: "You can't catch me!"

"Now remember, don't fly too high!" called Daedalus, but his words were drowned by the screaming of the gulls.

I'm the first boy ever to fly! I'm making history! I shall be famous! thought Icarus, as he flew up and up, higher and higher.

At last Icarus was looking the sun itself in the face. "Think you're the highest thing in the sky, do you?" he jeered. "I can fly just as high as you! Higher, even!" He did not notice the drops of sweat on his forehead: He was so determined to outfly the sun.

Soon its vast heat beat on his face and on his back and on the great wings stuck on with wax. The wax softened. The wax trickled. The wax dripped. One feather came unstuck. Then a plume of feathers fluttered slowly down.

Icarus stopped flapping his wings. His father's words came back to him clearly now: *"Don't fly too close to the sun!"*

With a great sucking noise, the wax on his shoulders came unstuck. Icarus tried to catch hold of the wings, but they just folded up in his hands. He plunged down, his two fists full of feathers—down and down and down.

The clouds did not stop his fall.

The sea gulls did not catch him in their beaks.

His own father could only watch as Icarus hurtled head first into the glittering sea and sank deep down among the sharks and eels and squid. And all that was left of proud Icarus was a litter of waxy feathers floating on the sea.

Meet the Author

Geraldine McCaughrean

McCaughrean was very shy as a child in London, but she loved to make up stories. When her fourteen-year-old brother wrote a book, she wanted to be an author too. She kept writing while working many other jobs. In 1988, she finally became a full-time author. McCaughrean loves drama. She sometimes gets story ideas from plays. She lives in Berkshire, England, with her husband and daughter. Her dog, Daisy, likes to eat her stories instead of reading them.

Meet the Illustrator

Emma Chichester Clark

Clark was born in London, England. She draws the eyes of most of her characters in a very distinctive way—as circles with pupil dots. This gives the character a childlike, curiously expressive appearance. Many of Clark's books, such as *Tea with Aunt Augusta,* show characters wearing wide-brimmed hats. Expressive eyes and wide-brimmed hats are the trademarks of Emma Chichester Clark.

CALIFORNIA

READING: COMPREHENSION AND ANALYSIS OF GRADE-LEVEL-APPROPRIATE TEXT
2.5 Compare and contrast information on the same topic after reading several passages or articles. READING: STRUCTURAL FEATURES OF LITERATURE **3.2** Identify the main events of the plot, their causes, and the influence of each event on future actions. **3.3** Use knowledge of the situation and setting and of a character's traits and motivations to determine the causes for that character's actions.

Theme Connections

Discuss

Within the Selection

1. Why do Daedalus and Icarus risk their lives to leave the comfort of the palace?

2. Icarus ignores his father's advice and flies too close to the sun. Do you think he realized he was taking a risk?

Across Selections

3. How is the risk taken by Icarus similar to the risk taken by Jeremy in "Mrs. Frisby and the Crow"?

4. Compare the risks taken by the Crafts in "Two Tickets to Freedom" to the risks taken by Daedalus and Icarus.

Beyond the Selection

5. How does "Daedalus and Icarus" add to what you know about risks and consequences?

6. Why do daredevils take risks?

Write

Write about a time you took a risk you were warned not to take.

Read

Find books or magazine articles about people who have either taken foolish risks or avoided them altogether.

HISTORY-SOCIAL SCIENCE 4.5.3 Describe the similarities and differences among federal, state, and local governments. HISTORY-SOCIAL SCIENCE 4.5.4 Explain the structures and functions of state governments, including the roles and responsibilities of their elected officials.

Social Studies Link

Checks and Balances

Genre

Expository Text tells people something. It contains facts about real people, things, or events.

Text Feature

Diagrams are drawings that explain how something works.

The founders of America had a brilliant idea for running the government. They felt that one person should not have too much control. The power of the government was divided into three branches: executive, legislative, and judicial. Each branch has its own responsibilities, but they all work together. California's government also has these three branches.

California's executive branch is headed by the governor. The governor signs bills that become state laws. The power to veto a bill belongs to the governor as well. Making sure that the state laws are followed is also part of the governor's job.

The legislative branch of California has two houses: the Assembly and Senate. The members are elected by citizens. Members represent the people of their state. They write and vote on bills that might become a law. Helping people who have a problem with the federal government is another responsibility.

The California Supreme Court and lower courts are part of the judicial branch. There is one chief justice and six associate justices on the California Supreme Court. They decide arguments and hear appeals about laws. Lower courts must follow the decisions of the state supreme court.

Understanding your state's government is important for everyone. Citizens play a vital role in their government. How can you be part of the state government?

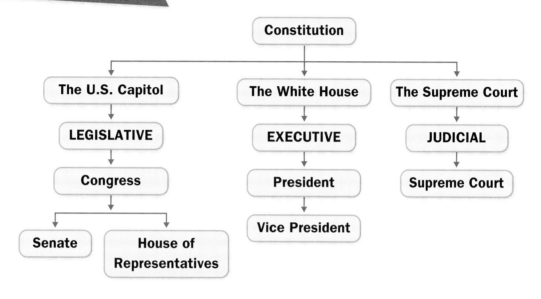

1. Read the information in the diagram. How are the national government and state governments similar? How are they different?

2. Which branch of government would you go to if you wanted to get a new law passed? Which branch of government would you use to get a law changed?

3. Create a diagram of California's state government that is similar to this diagram of the national government.

CALIFORNIA WebLink

Visit **www.ImagineItReading.com/ AtHome** for more information about the different branches of government.

Apply

Diagrams As you work on your investigation, think about how drawings can explain how something works.

The Dream Keeper

by Langston Hughes

Jacob Lawrence. *The Life of Harriet Tubman, #4.*
Casein tempera on hardboard. 12 x 17 7/8 inches.
Hampton University Museum, Hampton, Virginia.

Bring me all of your dreams,
You dreamers,
Bring me all of your
Heart melodies
That I may wrap them
In a blue cloud-cloth
Away from the too-rough fingers
Of the world.

114

Dreams

BY LANGSTON HUGHES

Hold fast to dreams
For if dreams die
Life is a broken-winged bird
That cannot fly.
Hold fast to dreams
For when dreams go
Life is a barren field
Frozen with snow.

William H. Johnson. *Midnight Sun, Lofoten.*
Oil on burlap. 41 4/8 x 59 1/8 inches.
Smithsonian American Art Museum, Washington, D.C.

115

Focus Questions What is freedom?
Why do people risk their lives for freedom?

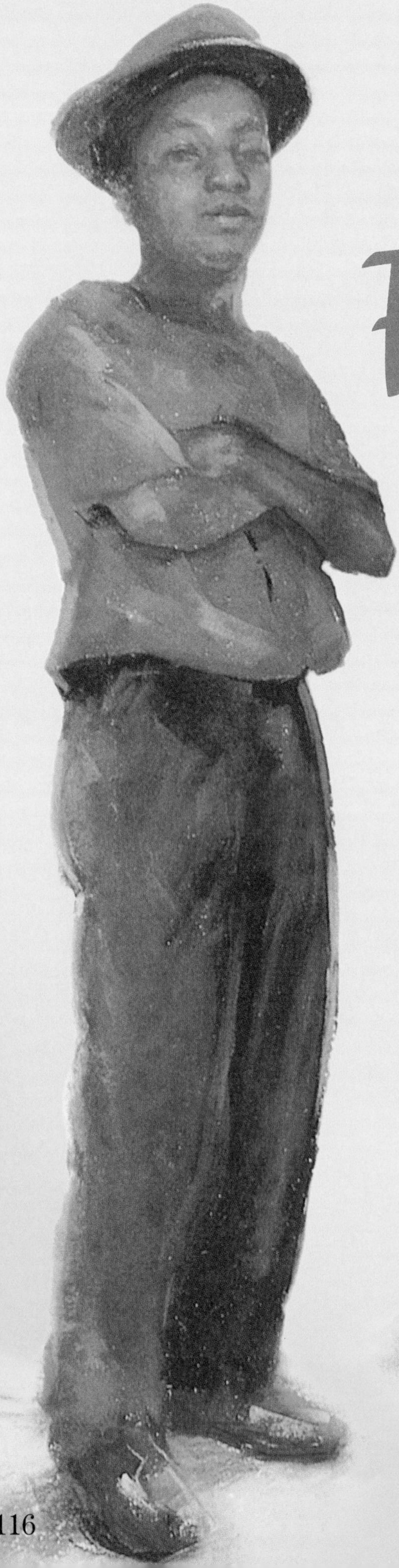

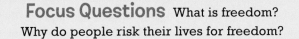

Freedom

by Langston Hughes
illustrated by Tyrone Geter

Freedom will not come
Today, this year
    Nor ever
Through compromise and fear.
I have as much right
As the other fellow has
    To stand
On my two feet
And own the land.

I tire so of hearing people say,
Let things take their course.
Tomorrow is another day.
I do not need my freedom when I'm dead.
I cannot live on tomorrow's bread.
    Freedom
    Is a strong seed
    Planted
    In a great need.
    I live here, too.
    I want freedom
    Just as you.

Test-Taking Strategy: Writing an Answer to a Question

Sometimes you will be asked to write an answer on a test. The answer might be as short as one sentence or as long as a page. Make sure you read the directions and question carefully so you know what you are supposed to do.

Writing an Answer to a Question

Read these directions and questions. They could follow a story that you might read on a test. Think about what you should do.

> How are the two soccer players DIFFERENT in the way that they prepared for the game? Use details and information from the story to support your answer.

The story was probably about two soccer players getting ready for a game. That means **you should answer the question based on what you read**. You also should focus on how the two players prepared for the game. When you write your answer, you should use details from the story.

Here is a different kind of writing task.

> Your town does not have a skateboard park. You and your friends want the town to build one. Write a letter to the mayor explaining why the town should build a skateboard park.

This task asks for your ideas. You do not have to read a story to complete the task. You need to think about the topic, and write a letter about your thoughts on it. Plan your writing before you begin. Think about what you want to say. Write so the reader understands you.

Test-Taking Practice

Read the story "The Racing Leg." Then answer Numbers 1 through 4.

It did not seem fair. I looked at Abby, who was trying to kick the ball. After two tries, Abby made a decent kick. She turned on her good leg and hurried toward first base.

"Way to go, Abby," said Ms. Marston, our teacher.

"Ms. Marston, you are the best," I said. "Abby really likes the way you challenge her to work harder."

Ms. Marston looked at me and said, "It wouldn't be right to treat her differently than the other students."

After gym class, I walked with Abby to our next class. Before we got there, Mr. Wyatt stopped us. He led us to the auditorium.

"If I hadn't been in the car accident, I could play better," Abby said. "Now we have to listen to people tell us how to be winners." Abby pointed at her prosthesis. "How would they feel if they had this?"

Ten minutes later, though, Abby was on the edge of her seat. The speakers were from a challenged athletes organization. The first speaker, Chris, had his legs removed because of a rare disease. He won a gold medal at the Paralympic Games. These are similar to the Olympics but are for people with physical challenges.

After we left the auditorium, Abby said, "I'm not sure I could do that, Trina. I would be afraid of falling or making a fool of myself."

A few weeks later, Abby showed up at my house with a new racing leg. She had decided to get one after all.

"If I fall, I fall. It is a risk I'm willing to take." Abby looked determined, as though she could do anything.

For months, Abby trained with a coach. She had to learn to run using her new leg. She fell almost every day, but she kept at it. She finally felt good enough to enter a race. It was a little more than three miles. This was a big step for a girl who could hardly run to first base.

On the day of the race, Abby was afraid but decided to race anyway. I waited for her at the finish line.

Hundreds of people crossed the finish line, but not Abby. Finally the last group of runners arrived. Abby was among them. I thought she would be sad, but she had a big smile on her face. She ran over and gave me a hug.

"I fell a few times, but I finished," Abby said. "Next time, it will be a different story."

Use the information you learned from the story "The Racing Leg" to answer questions 1 through 4. Write your answers on a piece of paper.

1. This story is *most* like a

   A science fiction story.

   B fable.

   C tall tale.

   D true story.

2. What did Trina think was unfair?

   A Mr. Wyatt's class was cancelled.

   B Abby could not play kickball well.

   C They had to go to an assembly.

   D Abby did not win the race.

3. Why did Abby need special training?

   A Her new leg was different from her old leg.

   B She was not able to play kickball very well.

   C The race was too far for her to run.

   D Almost all the other runners were faster.

4. Which of these will *most* likely happen next?

   A Abby's parents will be disappointed.

   B Trina will get bored and go home.

   C Abby will keep training.

   D Trina will win a race.

Test Tips

- Read the directions carefully.

- Read each question carefully.

- Skim the story, but do not try to memorize it.

Nature's Delicate Balance

Nature has a way of keeping things in balance.
Plants and animals depend on each other
to live. Water and food are used over and
over again in nature's great recycling system.
Energy is passed from one living thing to
another in food webs all over the world. How
does nature's delicate balance affect you?
What happens when that balance is disrupted?

Fine Art Theme Connection

Look at the painting *The Olbatos
Ravine* by Roberto Montenegro.

- How does Montenegro use
  color to show different features
  of the landscape?

- How does the painting suggest
  nature's delicate balance?

Roberto Montenegro.
The Olbatos Ravine. 1967.

Oil on canvas. 32 x 26 cm. National Bank
of Mexico Collection, Mexico City, Mexico.

BIG Idea

What role do you play in nature's delicate balance?

123

CALIFORNIA

READING: VOCABULARY AND CONCEPT DEVELOPMENT 1.3 Use knowledge of root words to determine the meaning of unknown words within a passage.

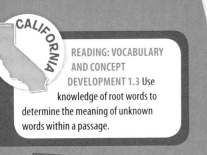

Read the story to find the meanings of these words, which are also in "The Snowflake: A Water Cycle Story":

✦ reservoir
✦ glacier
✦ jagged
✦ raging
✦ brook
✦ condensing
✦ particles
✦ droplet
✦ irrigation
✦ flowed
✦ trickled
✦ torrent

Vocabulary Development

Context Clues are hints in the text that help you find the meanings of words. Look at the words *reservoir* and *trickled*. Use context clues to find each word's meaning.

124

Vocabulary
Warm-Up

Matt's science class was taking a field trip to a big reservoir near the school. They had been studying the water cycle for the past two weeks. "Now it's time to see some water in action!" their teacher told them.

"Too bad we can't take a field trip to see a glacier!" Matt's friend, Ahman, joked. "I sure would love to climb those jagged peaks!"

"Too bad we can't go white-water rafting down a raging river," Becca said.

"Um, can't we just watch a leaf float down the brook in the park?" Gina asked timidly.

"That's no fun!" shouted Brandon.

Their teacher laughed. "Maybe next time we'll try the glacier. This time, I think we'll stick to water that's a little closer to home."

Sheila, a water expert, was their guide at the reservoir. "The reservoir catches the rainwater that falls to the ground after condensing in clouds," Sheila told them. "Then we remove the dirt particles from every droplet of water."

"What do you think the water from the reservoir is used for?" Sheila asked.

"Irrigation for crops," Kaitlyn answered.

"Water flowed from the hose when I helped my mom with her garden," added Annemarie.

"It trickled out of my kitchen faucet when I was washing dishes," Becca said.

"Water from the reservoir rushed out of my shower in a torrent this morning," Keegan said.

"Great answers," Sheila said.

"Water is a wonderful thing, that's for sure," said their teacher. "Now, who's ready to climb a glacier?"

Vocabulary Word Play

On a separate sheet of paper, create a poem using at least six of the vocabulary words. Share your poem with a partner.

Concept Vocabulary

This lesson's concept word is **process.** A *process* is the series of steps needed to make or to do something. Think of a task you do every day. No matter how small the activity, there are at least a few actions involved. Choose a task such as brushing your teeth, and make a list of the steps required to complete it. (Take toothbrush out of holder. Pick up tube of toothpaste. Unscrew lid, and so on.) Share your list of steps with a classmate.

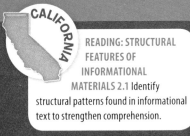

READING: STRUCTURAL FEATURES OF INFORMATIONAL MATERIALS 2.1 Identify structural patterns found in informational text to strengthen comprehension.

Genre

Narrative Nonfiction presents factual information in a narrative to make an exciting story.

Comprehension Skill

Sequence
As you read the selection, think about the order of events and how this helps you understand the selection.

The Snowflake

A Water Cycle Story

written and illustrated by Neil Waldman

Focus Questions

How does the water cycle work? How does the water cycle affect you?

JANUARY

On a moonless night, a tiny snowflake fell from a great gray cloud. It floated slowly downward with thousands of other flakes, coming to rest on the jagged peak of a mountain.

FEBRUARY

A wind whistled over the mountain, carrying the snowflake back up into the air. The snowflake twisted and spun, swirling into a pond on the mountainside. The snowflake melted into a droplet, but as the days grew colder the pond froze.

MARCH

As the sun grew warmer, the ice began to melt. The snowflake became a droplet of water once again. It fell through a crack in the rocky pond bottom and trickled down into the ground. Downward it sank, into the blackness within the mountain. Along with millions of other droplets, it splashed into an underground stream that flowed deep into the earth.

APRIL

After a long journey, the stream turned upward, bubbling through the ground in an icy spring. Sparkling in the sunlight, the droplet rushed into a brook. It danced around some stones, spilled over a waterfall, and surged into a raging river. The droplet flowed past villages and cities, under a great gray bridge where cars and buses carried people to and fro.

MAY

A shiny metal pump sucked the droplet through a maze of zigzagging pipes into the irrigation system of a nearby farm. It spun through a long rubber hose, swished into a spinning sprinkler, and squirted up into the air. The droplet flew in a great arc, landing at last on the leaf of a cabbage plant.

JUNE

In the chill of morning, a heavy blanket of fog rolled in over the farm. The droplet slowly evaporated and floated up into the thick grayness. But soon the rising sun began to bake the air as the fog rose high into the sky and became a cloud.

JULY

The cloud joined a mass of darkening storm clouds. Lightning flashed, thunder rumbled, and a torrent of raindrops dived toward the earth. The droplet rocketed downward and splashed into the clear waters of a reservoir. It was sucked through a series of filters that removed all the dirt particles until only pure water remained.

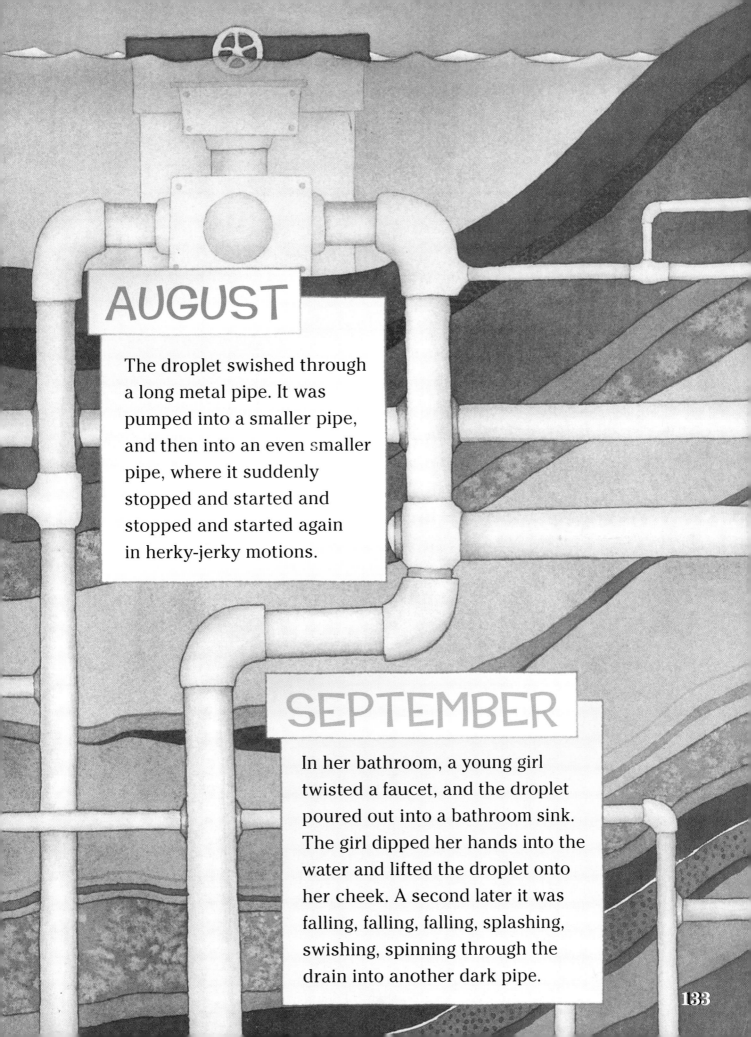

AUGUST

The droplet swished through a long metal pipe. It was pumped into a smaller pipe, and then into an even smaller pipe, where it suddenly stopped and started and stopped and started again in herky-jerky motions.

SEPTEMBER

In her bathroom, a young girl twisted a faucet, and the droplet poured out into a bathroom sink. The girl dipped her hands into the water and lifted the droplet onto her cheek. A second later it was falling, falling, falling, splashing, swishing, spinning through the drain into another dark pipe.

133

OCTOBER

After a long, dark journey, the droplet poured out into the ocean. It flowed past fields of waving sea grasses, over corals of many colors, and into the mouth of a great striped fish. Passing through the fish's body, the droplet returned to the sea.

NOVEMBER

Rising up to the ocean's surface the droplet was pulled steadily toward the shore. On the crest of a mighty wave it bubbled into foam, crashing onto the sandy beach of a tropical island.

DECEMBER

In the sunlight of a winter's morning, the droplet evaporated. It rose into the air, entering a great gray cloud. A whistling wind pushed the cloud across the sea, past cities and towns, beyond an icy spring, and over a raging river. It drifted past a waterfall and a frozen pond. On a moonless night, a tiny snowflake fell from the cloud. It floated slowly downward with thousands of other flakes, coming to rest on the jagged peak of a mountain.

For years and years, water has been freezing, melting, evaporating, condensing, and freezing again. It travels all over the world, and in its many forms, water has been around far longer than people have. In fact, water has been here almost as long as the earth itself. So the next time you throw a snowball, or jump into a swimming pool, or drink some ice water on a hot summer's day, stop and think for a moment . . .

because some of that very water might have tumbled over Niagara Falls, or risen as morning mist in the steaming jungles of Africa, or lay frozen for centuries inside a glacier on the North Pole. It might have

been sipped by your great-grandmother in a cup of afternoon tea. It might have been used by Abraham Lincoln to scrub his hands before dinner in the White House. It might even have been guzzled by a thirsty Tyrannosaurus rex in a prehistoric swamp millions of years ago.

Meet the Author and Illustrator

Neil Waldman

Waldman is an artist who has won many awards. His paintings are in important buildings around the world. Even though he is famous, Waldman loves to take time out to visit schools. He tells students about his life as an artist or how he worked on a book. Usually he lets students ask him questions. Waldman loves traveling and even got to live in Israel for a while. He grew up in New York, which is where he lives today.

CALIFORNIA

WRITING: ORGANIZATION AND FOCUS 1.1 Select a focus, an organization structure, and a point of view based upon purpose, audience, length, and format requirements. **HISTORY-SOCIAL SCIENCE 4.4.7** Trace the evolution of California's water system into a network of dams, aqueducts, and reservoirs.

Theme Connections

Discuss

Within the Selection

1. What different forms can water take?

2. What happens to rain after it falls into a reservoir?

Beyond the Selection

3. What are some ways you use water?

4. What would Earth be like without water?

Write

Write a descriptive paragraph about a rainy day.

Read

Look for books and magazine articles about the evolution of California's water system and its network of dams, aqueducts, and reservoirs.

CALIFORNIA

SCIENCE: EARTH SCIENCES
5.a Students know changes in the earth are due to slow processes, such as erosion, and some changes are due to rapid processes, such as landslides, volcanic eruptions, and earthquakes. 5.b Students know natural processes, including freezing and thawing and the growth of roots, cause rocks to break down into smaller pieces. 5.c Students know moving water erodes landforms, reshaping the land by taking it away from some places and depositing it as pebbles, sand, silt, and mud in other places (weathering, transport, and deposition).

Science Link

Genre

Expository Text tells people something. It contains facts about real people, things, or events.

Text Feature

Headings tell readers what a paragraph is going to be about.

Erosion and Landslides

The surface of Earth changes all the time. Erosion and landslides are two important forces of change.

Erosion

Wind and water can wear away Earth's surface. This happens over long periods of time. These changes are called erosion. These forces of nature transport particles of soil and rock from one place and deposit them somewhere else as pebbles, silt, sand, and mud.

Wind can only move the lightest pieces of rock. Water that has flowed in one place over a period of time can erode bigger pieces of soil and rock. Ice helps the process of erosion. When water gets between rocks and freezes, the ice pushes on the rocks and breaks them apart.

Plants can also contribute to erosion. When a tree's large roots push through the earth below, they can rub against rocks and break them into smaller pieces.

Landslides

Landslides occur suddenly when dirt, rocks, or mud fall down a slope. Earthquakes or heavy rain can cause landslides. When soil turns to mud, it becomes heavy and slippery, so it flows downward. This is called a mudslide.

Think Link

1. There are two headings in the article you just read: Erosion and Landslides. If you could add another heading to this selection, what would it be? What would you write about in the paragraphs that fit under your new heading?

2. Do erosion and landslides change Earth rapidly or slowly? What happens to the rock and soil that gets displaced?

3. How do ice and plants play a role in the process of erosion?

CALIFORNIA WebLink

Visit **www.ImagineItReading.com/ AtHome** for more information about erosion and landslides.

Apply

Headings As you work on your investigation, think about how graphs can help you explain your ideas.

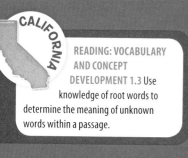

READING: VOCABULARY AND CONCEPT DEVELOPMENT 1.3 Use knowledge of root words to determine the meaning of unknown words within a passage.

Read the story to find the meanings of these words, which are also in "Energy Makes Things Happen":

+ **windmills**
+ **release**
+ **eventually**
+ **energy**
+ **remains**
+ **trace**
+ **fuels**
+ **creates**
+ **stored**
+ **contains**
+ **transferred**
+ **soar**

Vocabulary Development

Context Clues are hints in the text that help you find the meanings of words. Look at the words *release* and *fuels*. Use context clues to find each word's meaning.

Vocabulary

Warm-Up

Emilie walked with her sister Charlotte, her parents, and her grandpa to the park that is three blocks from her house. She and Charlotte asked whether they could run ahead to see the windmills near the park. "You guys are walking too slowly!" Emilie protested.

"It doesn't help that we adults are carrying everything!" her mother said, laughing.

"You two are like little ponies chomping at the bit," said their dad. "I release you from your stalls! Run and gallop to freedom!"

"We will catch up eventually," their mom said.

"Where do those two get all their energy?" Grandpa asked with a laugh.

When they got to the park, Emilie helped her dad clean the remains off the grill. She made sure that no trace of old food was left. Her dad then placed pieces of charcoal on the small metal grill.

"Shanna's family has a big gas grill," Emilie said.

"I personally like charcoal more than other fuels," said Grandpa. "It creates such a delicious smell."

Charlotte and Emilie started rummaging through the basket where the snacks were stored.

"All I want is the bag that contains the strawberries!" Emilie said. "Oh no! Mom, they are not in here!"

"It's OK. I transferred them to the cooler," said Mom.

It was not long before Dad and Grandpa brought a steaming plate of perfectly grilled chicken to the table.

"Look!" Grandpa said. "Watch that eagle soar above the trees. Aren't they amazing creatures?"

"Sure they are," Emilie said, "as long as they don't swoop down and snatch our chicken! I am starving!"

Vocabulary Word Play

Working with a partner, create sentences using alliteration and the vocabulary words. Share your sentences with the class.

Concept Vocabulary

This lesson's concept word is **transform.** *Transform* means "to change from one thing to another." In movies and comic books, ordinary people transform into superheroes. In real life, caterpillars transform into butterflies. Make up a creature or person who transforms into someone or something else. Describe your character and its transformation to a classmate.

READING: NARRATIVE
ANALYSIS OF GRADE-
LEVEL-APPROPRIATE TEXT
3.2 Identify the main events of
the plot, their causes, and the influence of
each event on future actions.

Genre

Expository Text
tells people something. It
contains facts about real
people, things, or events.

Comprehension Skill

⭐ **Main Idea
and Details**
As you read, look for
the main idea the author is
trying to get across. Then
look for the details she uses
to support the main idea.

Energy Makes Things Happen

by Kimberly Brubaker Bradley

Focus Questions

What is the main source of energy for living things on Earth? How can energy be transferred from one form to another?

The sun shines in the sky. Two children run with a kite. A boy sails a boat across a pond. A girl hits a baseball. A family cooks hot dogs on a campfire. A big rock sits high on a hill.

All these things have different kinds of energy.

Energy makes things happen. It can make things hot or bright or loud. It can make things move. Energy can be used to do work.

There are many different kinds of energy. When the sun shines, it gives us light. The sun also gives us heat. Both heat and light are kinds of energy.

When you run or jump or hop or skip, that's energy too. Everything that moves uses energy.

Energy is transferred from one thing to another. When a boy throws a baseball, he transfers energy from his arm to the ball. Then the ball can move through the air. (The more energy he gives the ball, the faster it goes!)

When a girl swings a bat, she transfers energy from her arms to the bat. When the bat hits the ball, the energy in the bat goes into the ball and sends it flying.

Wind is air that moves—it's air with energy. The energy from wind lifts kites into the sky. It makes windmills go around and hot-air balloons soar. Wind energy sails sailboats across a pond.

Things that release energy as they are burned are
called fuels. Gasoline, oil, and wood are all fuels. When
we put gasoline into a car, we are putting fuel into it.
As the car runs, its engine burns the gasoline. The
gasoline gets used up. The energy from the gasoline
makes the car go forward.

When we build a campfire to cook hot dogs, we are
burning wood fuel to turn its stored energy into heat
energy for the hot dogs.

But the hot dogs are also a kind of fuel! Our bodies need energy, and they get it from the food we eat. Strawberries, rutabagas, potato salad, milk, popcorn, tuna fish, and hot dogs—everything we eat gets used up by our bodies.

Our food is the fuel that gives us the energy to run and play. Food gives us energy to do our work.

You may not think a glass of milk contains energy. Milk is not moving or doing work. It's not hot. It doesn't give off light. But milk has energy stored inside it. All fuels do.

Remember the rock on the hill? It has energy inside it too. It's not hot or moving, and it isn't a fuel—you can't eat it or drink it or burn it. BUT—if you gave the rock a tiny push, it would roll all the way down the hill. It would turn its stored energy into moving energy.

A rock at the bottom of a hill does not have stored energy to turn into moving energy. If you push it, it doesn't fall anywhere. But if you roll the rock all the way to the top of the hill, you give it the energy to fall back down the hill. The energy you use to push it up the hill stays with the rock, waiting, so that eventually the rock can fall back down the hill.

The rock might sit on the hill for a long time. It can't fall back down until someone or something gives it a little push. Then it can fall a long way. Many things need a little bit of energy to help them give off a lot of energy. A candle stores energy, but it doesn't burn until it's lit. A carrot stores energy, but it can't give it out until you eat it.

We can see how energy got into the rock—someone pushed it up the hill. But how did energy get into the carrot? Or into gasoline, or into any of our fuels?

Most of our energy comes from the sun. The sun gives off so much energy that even though it is very far away, a lot of its heat and light reach the earth.

The energy from the sun makes plants grow. So the carrot contains energy from the sun. The sun's energy makes grass grow. Cows eat the grass and get energy to make milk.

So the milk and the cows contain energy from the sun. We drink milk and get the energy to take care of the cows! And to push rocks up hills. The energy we get from our food first came from the sun.

The energy in gasoline first came from the sun too. Gasoline is made from a fossil fuel. Fossil fuels are made from the remains of plants and animals that lived long ago. The sun gave these plants and animals energy to grow.

Coal, natural gas, and oil are fossil fuels.

The sun warms us and gives us light. It warms the air and creates the wind. The sun gives off a lot of energy.

Energy never disappears. It can move from one object—such as a baseball bat—to another—such as a ball. Energy can move from the sun to a carrot to a child to a rock. It can flow from light into a plant, from a plant into a fuel, from a fuel into the movement of a car going down the street—but energy never goes away.

That's good, because we need lots of energy. Without it, we couldn't move! We wouldn't have light or heat—we wouldn't grow. Nothing could. Without energy, we wouldn't have anything. We need energy to make things happen!

FIND OUT MORE ABOUT ENERGY

Moving Cars

Energy can be transferred from one object to another. Here's how you can see it happen.

First, get two small toy cars (blocks or marbles would work fine, too, but cars are easier to use). Set one toy car by itself in the middle of a hard surface, like a smooth floor or a table. Now take the second car and give it a push so that it rolls into the back of the first car. (Don't hold on to the second car.) *Bam!*

What happens to the first car? Does it move? Did the motion require energy? Where did the energy come from? What happens to the second car? Where did ITS energy come from?

Now get a third car. Line the first two up so they are touching, back to front. Take the third car and roll it into the back of the second car just like you did before.

What happens? Which cars move? Which moves the farthest?

The energy from the moving car gets transferred to the nonmoving car. When there are three cars, the energy is transferred from the first car to the second, and then from the second to the third—all faster than you can blink!

Back to the Sun

Think of something—anything—that uses energy. Can you trace this energy back to the sun? Pretend you are playing baseball. Your body would have to move, and that would require energy. Where does your body get the energy?

From the food you eat. Let's say you ate a toasted cheese sandwich for lunch right before you played baseball. Where did the energy in the sandwich come from?

The cheese was made from milk, the bread from wheat. Wheat is a plant—it gets its energy to grow from the sun. Cows make milk, but of course it takes energy for them to do so. Where do they get the energy? From the food they eat. What do they eat? Grass. Where does the grass get the energy to grow? From the sun. So the energy it takes for you to play baseball originally came from the sun.

This is a fun game to play. If you think hard enough, you'll find out that almost all the energy we use on earth first came from the sun.

Meet the Author

Kimberly Brubaker Bradley

Bradley loves science and studied it in college. College was also where Bradley learned to love writing. After college, she wrote for magazines. She worked as an editor and chemist. In 1988, she wrote her first book. Since then, she has written one or more books every year. Bradley feels at home on her large farm in Bristol, where Tennessee and Virginia meet. Mountains fill the skyline. Bradley, her husband, daughter, and son, live there with ponies, dogs, sheep, and a cat.

Theme Connections

Discuss

Within the Selection

1. Where does most of our energy come from, and how do we get energy from that source?

2. What are some useful things wind energy can do?

Across Selections

3. What do water and energy have in common?

4. How are fossil fuels used in "Two Tickets to Freedom"?

Beyond the Selection

5. Think of your favorite food. Try to trace its energy back to the sun.

6. What things do you do that require the most energy?

Write

Tell about a time you felt like you were out of energy.

Read

Look for books and magazine articles about how energy is conserved and used by the state of California.

CALIFORNIA

SCIENCE: LIFE SCIENCES
3.c Students know many plants depend on animals for pollination and seed dispersal, and animals depend on plants for food and shelter.

Science Link

Genre

Expository Text tells people something. It contains facts about real people, things, or events.

Text Feature

Charts present information in an organized and visual way.

Helping Each Other Survive

Plants and animals are very dependent on each other. Many plants rely on animals for pollination and seed dispersal. Animals need plants for food and shelter.

Insects and birds help plants reproduce by carrying pollen. Plants produce pollen and nectar, a sugary liquid, which many insects and birds feed on. When they feed on a plant, some of the sticky pollen clings to their bodies. As they move to other flowers, the pollen gets transferred to the flowers of other plants. This pollen is used by the plant to make new seeds.

After seeds are produced, plants need a way to get the seeds to new locations so they can spread and survive. Some seeds have tiny hooks that attach to the fur of passing animals. Other seeds are encased in sweet fruits that animals eat.

Animals often take their food to a safer location and discard the pit, or seed, after eating the fruit around it. If the seeds are small, they are swallowed whole and then excreted, usually far away from the original plant. The seeds will eventually grow into new plants that will provide food and shelter for more animals.

Think Link

How Plants Are Pollinated and Seeds Are Distributed	
Step 1	Plants produce nectar and pollen.
Step 2	Insects and birds visit plants to eat nectar and pollen.
Step 3	Pollen attaches to insects and birds as they fly away.
Step 4	Pollen is dropped on other plants and is used to make seeds.
Step 5	Fruit forms around seeds.
Step 6	Animals carry fruit away and eat it.
Step 7	Pits and seeds are dropped.
Step 8	Seeds grow into new plants away from the original plants.

1. Look at the chart above. Much of the information in the chart is the same as the information in the expository text. How does the chart aid your understanding of the text?

2. How do plants help animals survive? How do animals help plants survive?

3. Can you think of other ways that seeds could be spread?

WebLink

Visit **www.ImagineItReading.com/ AtHome** for more information about how pollination works.

Apply

Charts As you work on your investigation, think about how charts can present information in an organized and visual way.

CALIFORNIA

READING: VOCABULARY AND CONCEPT DEVELOPMENT 1.2 Apply knowledge of word origins, derivations, synonyms, antonyms, and idioms to determine the meaning of words and phrases.

Read the article to find the meanings of the words, which are also in "Who Eats What?":

✦ **bitterly**
✦ **harbor**
✦ **feast**
✦ **seaweed**
✦ **spiny**
✦ **urchins**
✦ **seafloor**
✦ **depend**
✦ **food chain**
✦ **branch**
✦ **linked**
✦ **food web**

Vocabulary Development

Word Analysis gives us clues about a word's meaning. The meaning often changes when a prefix or a suffix is added to a root word. Use word analysis to define *bitterly* and *linked*.

160

Vocabulary

Warm-Up

Pretend you are a scientist who has decided to take a trip to Antarctica. You will be going with five friends who want to learn more about the wildlife on this remote continent. Normally, Antarctica is bitterly cold. During January, it will be slightly warmer. This is the summer season in this part of the world.

The boat trip is long. You finally arrive at the harbor of your research site. You set up your microscope and other equipment. You cannot wait to explore!

You venture out onto the ice, cut a hole, and start fishing. You have quite a bit of luck because the icy waters overflow with life during the summer. You can study some of the fish, feast on others, and collect several kinds of seaweed and spiny sea urchins as well. This could be difficult if you have to travel down to the seafloor.

One of your friends points to a group of ten penguins. Look at them play! They are diving in and out of the water in search of a meal. These penguins depend on fish for energy. The cold environment limits their options in the food chain.

The group decides to branch off in different directions. Each of you will see what you can find. You take walkie-talkies, just in case someone spots something unique.

This is a fascinating ecosystem, you think to yourself. You see seals, penguins, gulls, and even see a pod of whales. It is amazing how every creature is linked together in the food web and in the cycle of life.

Vocabulary Word Play

Get into a group, and write one of the words in the diamond. Think of three synonyms for each word, and write them in the ovals. If no one can think of a synonym for a word, think of an antonym for it, and write it in one of the boxes.

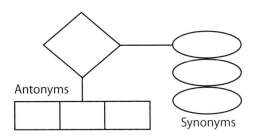

Antonyms

Synonyms

Concept Vocabulary

This lesson's concept word is **photosynthesis.** *Photosynthesis* is the process by which green plants combine carbon dioxide, water, and sunlight to produce food. Plants take carbon dioxide from the air and produce oxygen, which makes the air fresher for people to breathe. Think of three other reasons why plants are important to us and our life on Earth.

CALIFORNIA

SCIENCE: LIFE SCIENCES
2.a Students know plants are the primary source of matter and energy entering most food chains. 2.b Students know producers and consumers (herbivores, carnivores, omnivores, and decomposers) are related in food chains and food webs and may compete with each other for resources in an ecosystem. 3.c Students know many plants depend on animals for pollination and seed dispersal, and animals depend on plants for food and shelter.

Genre

Expository Text tells people something. It contains facts about real people, things, or events.

Comprehension Skill

☆ **Making Inferences**
As you read, use personal experience as well as details from the text to understand something the author left unsaid.

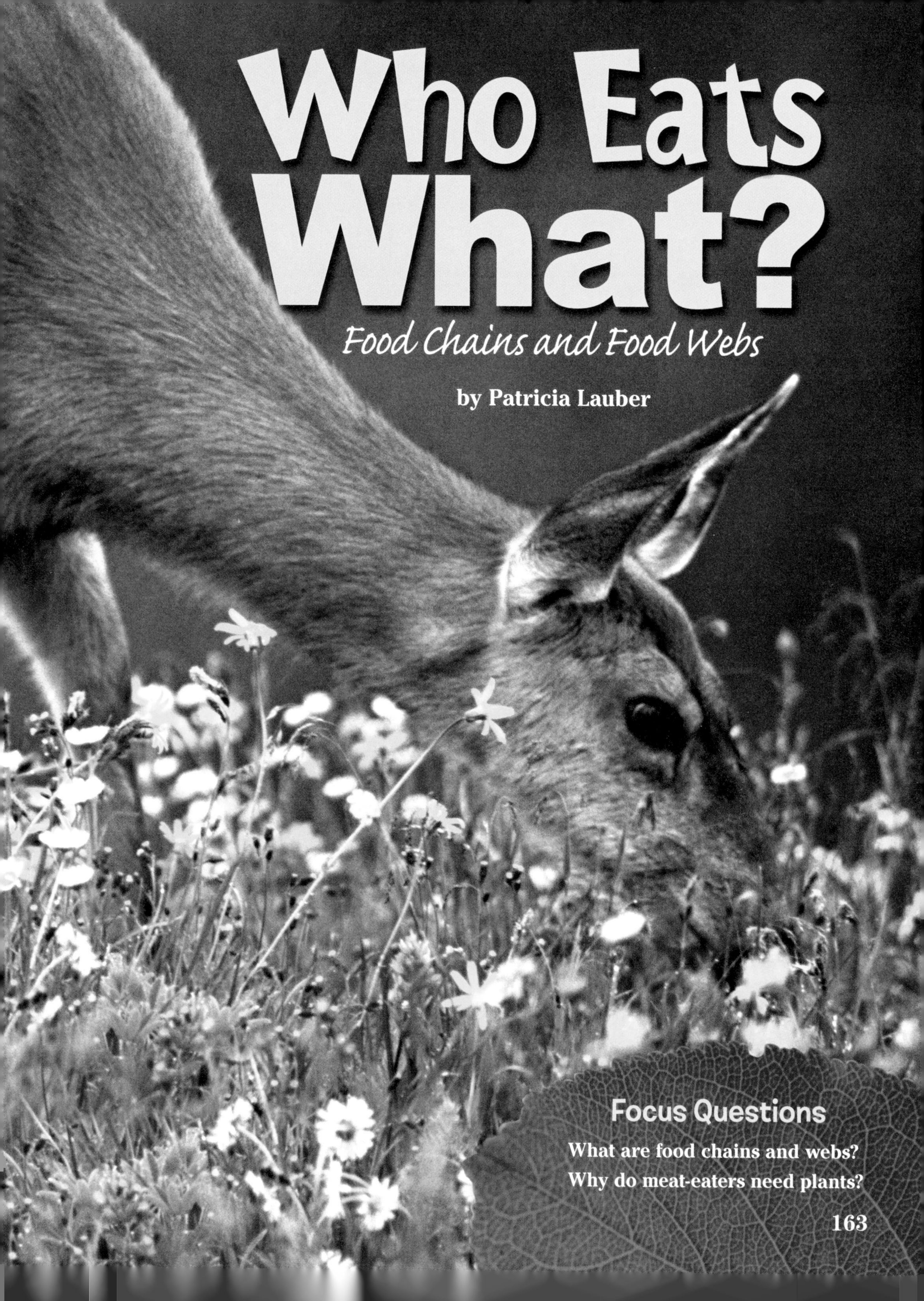

Who Eats What?

Food Chains and Food Webs

by Patricia Lauber

Focus Questions

What are food chains and webs?
Why do meat-eaters need plants?

A caterpillar is eating a leaf on an apple tree. Later the caterpillar is spotted by a wren. It becomes part of the wren's dinner. Still later the wren is eaten by a hawk. Leaf, caterpillar, wren, and hawk are all linked. Together they form a food chain. Each is a link in the chain.

The hawk is the top of the food chain, because no other animal attacks and eats hawks. The animal at the top of a food chain is always the last eater—the one nobody else eats.

Suppose you eat an apple off the tree. That makes you part of a short food chain—the apple and you. You are the top of the food chain.

Or suppose you drink a glass of milk. Now you are the top of a slightly longer food chain. The milk came from a cow, and the cow ate grass. So this chain is grass, cow, you.

Every time you eat a meal, you become the top of several food chains. You can draw a picture to show them. If you had a peanut-butter-and-jelly sandwich, a glass of milk, and an apple, the picture might look like this.

Food is the fuel our bodies need. Food keeps us alive. It gives us the energy we need to grow, move, and do many other things. The same thing is true for caterpillars, wrens, hawks—for all animals. All must find or catch the foods they need.

When you draw a food chain, you are drawing a flow of energy. The arrows show its path.

There are many, many food chains, more than anyone can count. But in one way they are all alike.

All food chains begin with green plants. Green plants are the only living things that can make their own food. They are the only living things that do not need to eat something else.

Green plants take energy from sunlight. They use it to make food out of water and air.

All animals depend on green plants for food, even animals that don't eat plants.

Hawks, for example, do not eat green plants. But the hawk ate the wren that ate the caterpillar that ate the leaf of a green plant. And so the hawk is linked to green plants through the food chain. It needs the plants as much as the caterpillar does.

Take a walk and look around. You will see parts of many food chains. Look at the leaves and flowers of plants. Look at the bark of trees. Look at fruits, nuts, and seeds that have fallen to the ground. What animals are eating them?

You might see a grasshopper
eating a blade of grass. You may not
see another animal eat the grasshopper.
But you can find out which animals eat
grasshoppers by going to the library. You can read up
on grasshoppers and any other animal you've seen.
You can draw food chains.

Your drawings will show that one plant may be the
start of several food chains. The leaves of an oak tree
may be food for caterpillars. Beetles may bore into the
tree's trunk. Acorns are food for squirrels, chipmunks,
blue jays, and deer.

The drawings will also show that most animals are
part of several food chains. Chipmunks, for example,
eat many foods. They eat nuts, seeds, berries, buds.
They may also eat insects, snails, and other small
animals.

And chipmunks themselves are eaten by weasels,
bobcats, foxes, coyotes, hawks. These animals may also
eat some of the things chipmunks eat.

Try drawing some of these food chains on one page. You will have arrows branching in all directions. Now you have drawn a food web. Food webs are made up of many food chains.

On land most food chains are short, but scientists still have much to learn about them. They have even more to learn about food chains in the seas. These chains are long. They are also hard to study, because most of the plants and animals live underwater.

In the water, as on the land, food chains begin with green plants. Some of the plants are tiny—you'd need a microscope to see them. Some are bigger.

The green plants are food for many tiny creatures, which become food for bigger creatures.

Small fish are eaten by bigger fish, which are eaten by still bigger fish, which are eaten by even bigger fish.

The biggest, such as tuna, are at the tops of food chains—unless they are caught by humans. Then one of them may turn up in your tuna-fish sandwich. Both the tuna and you are part of a food chain that began with a tiny green plant.

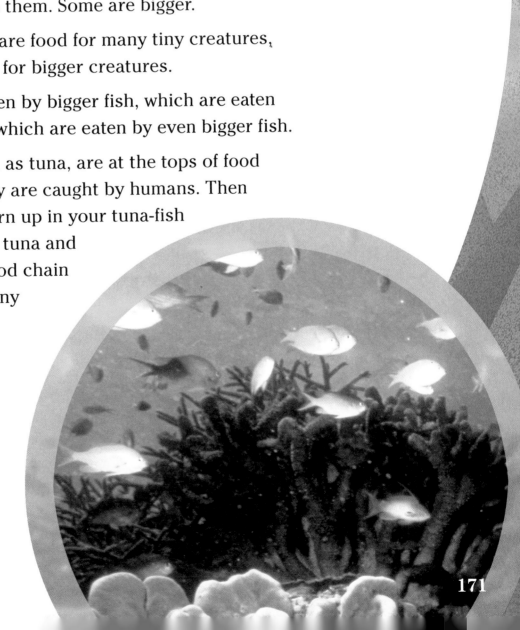

Food chains are found wherever life is found.

The far south of the world, Antarctica, is icy and bitterly cold for much of the year. But in summer its seas come alive. The water is rich with tiny green plants. They are fed on by tiny animals. And these are fed on by small animals such as krill, which look like shrimp. All these animals and plants are food for bigger animals, such as fish and squid.

Many other animals come to feast in these waters. There are seals, whales, and dolphins. There are many seabirds, among them penguins.

All the animals are linked to the tiny green plants.

The drawing shows a web of food chains at the far south of the world. The arrows show who eats what. Follow the arrows and find the animals that feed on krill—one of them is the blue whale, the biggest animal on earth. Find the animals that eat animals that eat krill.

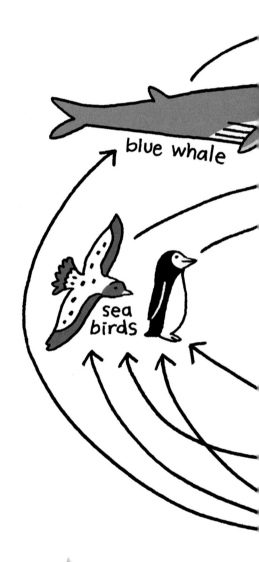

blue whale

sea birds

Sometimes people talk about catching krill
for human food. But what would happen to the
food web if fishermen took huge catches of krill
each year? To find out, look at the drawing again.

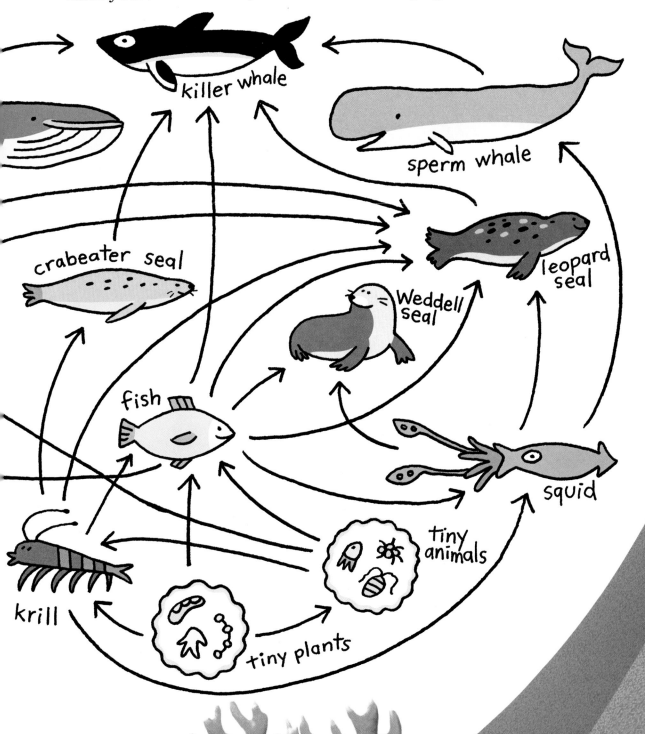

killer whale

sperm whale

crabeater seal

Weddell seal

leopard seal

fish

squid

krill

tiny animals

tiny plants

Humans often make changes in food chains and webs. Then they find that one change causes other changes. That was what happened when hunters killed nearly all the Pacific sea otters.

The otters lived off the west coast of North America. They lived in beds of giant seaweed, called kelp. Every year thousands of otters were killed for their fur. By the early 1900s almost none were left. But as the otters disappeared, so did beds of kelp. And so did eagles, harbor seals, and fish. What had happened? The answer lay in the kelp.

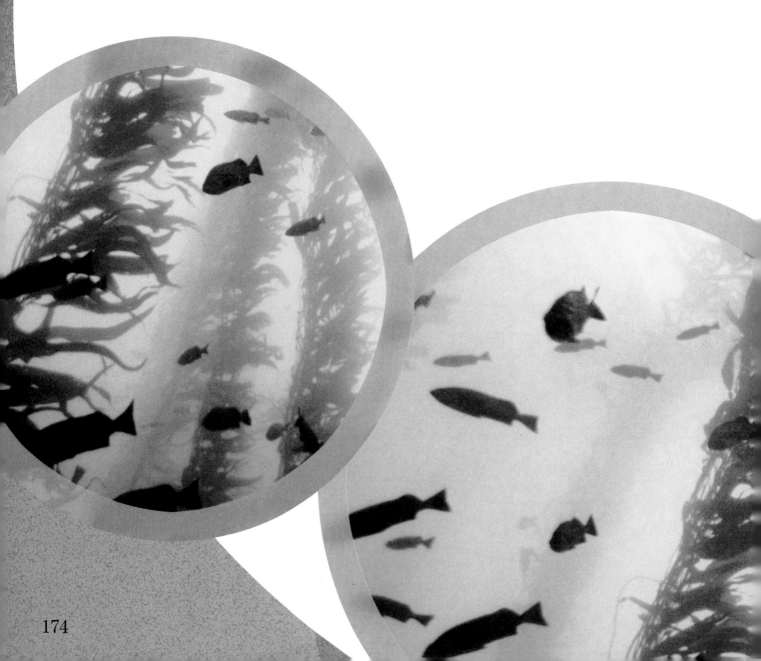

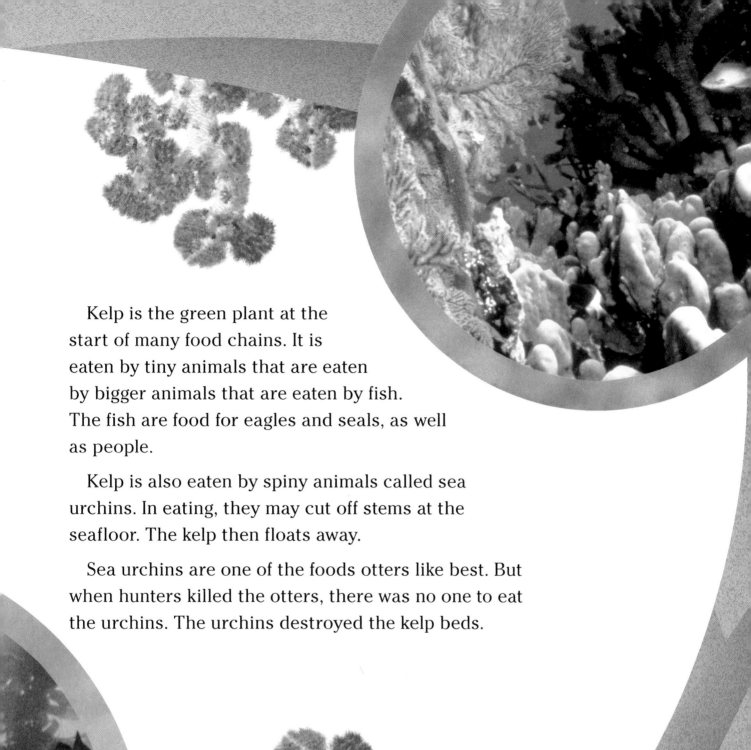

Kelp is the green plant at the
start of many food chains. It is
eaten by tiny animals that are eaten
by bigger animals that are eaten by fish.
The fish are food for eagles and seals, as well
as people.

Kelp is also eaten by spiny animals called sea
urchins. In eating, they may cut off stems at the
seafloor. The kelp then floats away.

Sea urchins are one of the foods otters like best. But
when hunters killed the otters, there was no one to eat
the urchins. The urchins destroyed the kelp beds.

Once the hunting stopped, the otters made a comeback. They ate sea urchins, and the kelp began to do well. When the kelp did well, the fish came back—and so did the eagles, seals, and fishermen.

All over the world, green plants and animals are linked in food chains that branch into food webs. A change in one link is felt up and down that chain. It is felt through the whole web.

And that's one good reason to take care of the earth—to take care of its plants and animals. When we help them, we also help ourselves. We too are part of many food webs.

Meet the Author

Patricia Lauber

Lauber says that she was "born wanting to write." Because she writes so many books about science, she has to do a lot of research. While doing research, she learns many new things. Lauber has also worked as an editor—a person who helps other writers make their work better. Born in New York City, she now lives in Connecticut with her husband. When she is not writing, Lauber likes to sail, hike, and go to plays.

READING: COMPREHENSION AND ANALYSIS OF GRADE-LEVEL-APPROPRIATE TEXT 2.4 Evaluate new information and hypotheses by testing them against known information and ideas. 2.5 Compare and contrast information on the same topic after reading several passages or articles. SCIENCE: LIFE SCIENCES 2.b Students know producers and consumers (herbivores, carnivores, omnivores, and decomposers) are related in food chains and food webs and may compete with each other for resources in an ecosystem.

Theme Connections

Discuss

Within the Selection

1. How are green plants different from other living things?
2. Describe what happens in the waters off Antarctica in the summer.

Across Selections

3. How is the information in "Energy Makes Things Happen" demonstrated in "Who Eats What?"
4. Who is at the top of the farmyard food chain in "Mrs. Frisby and the Crow"?

Beyond the Selection

5. Why are predators at the top of a food chain larger than the animals at the bottom of the food chain?
6. How can removing one link in a food web disrupt the entire system?

Write

Describe how you fit into a food web.

Read

Find books and magazine articles about food webs in different habitats in the state of California.

CALIFORNIA

SCIENCE: LIFE SCIENCES
2.a Students know plants are the primary source of matter and energy entering most food chains. 2.b Students know producers and consumers (herbivores, carnivores, omnivores, and decomposers) are related in food chains and food webs and may compete with each other for resources in an ecosystem. 3.c Students know many plants depend on animals for pollination and seed dispersal, and animals depend on plants for food and shelter.

Science Link

All Kinds of Eaters

Genre

Expository Text tells people something. It contains facts about real people, things, or events.

Text Feature

Captions explain what is happening in a photograph.

Plants make their own food by using energy from the sun. Because of this, plants are called producers. *Produce* means "to make." Without plants, animals would not exist.

Animals depend on plants or other animals for their energy. Animals are called consumers. *Consume* means "to eat."

There are three kinds of consumers. Animals that feast only on plants are called herbivores. *Herbi-* means "plant." Cows, sheep, rabbits, and mice are herbivores.

Animals that hunt and eat other animals are called carnivores. This includes animals that eat worms and bugs. *Carni-* means "meat." Tigers, wolves, sharks, and spiders are carnivores.

Animals that eat plants and meat are called omnivores. *Omni-* means "all." Humans are omnivores, as well as bears, raccoons, pigs, and flies.

The sun gives off light, and plants use it to make food. A giraffe eats plants, and a lion eats the giraffe. When the lion dies, its body rots and makes the soil rich. Plants grow in the soil, and the cycle begins again.

Think Link

1. A giraffe eating leaves

2. Giraffes running from danger

1. Look at the photographs and their captions. Think of two other photographs that would fit with this selection. What captions would you write for those two pictures?

2. Explain the difference between a producer and a consumer. Is a plant more of a producer or consumer in the food chain?

3. In your own words, explain how the food chain works. How do plants and animals depend on each other? How do they compete?

CALIFORNIA WebLink

Visit **www.ImagineItReading.com/AtHome** for more information about how carnivores, herbivores, and omnivores work together in a food chain.

Apply

Captions As you work on your investigation, think about a photo that you could use to illustrate your ideas. What caption would you write to accompany the photo?

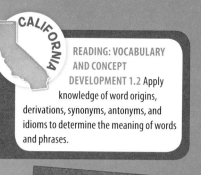

CALIFORNIA

READING: VOCABULARY AND CONCEPT DEVELOPMENT 1.2 Apply knowledge of word origins, derivations, synonyms, antonyms, and idioms to determine the meaning of words and phrases.

What Rot! Nature's Mighty Recycler

Read the story to find the meanings of these words, which are also in "What Rot! Nature's Mighty Recycler":

- ✦ teeming
- ✦ shrivel
- ✦ brittle
- ✦ circulate
- ✦ decays
- ✦ plump
- ✦ microbes
- ✦ enrich
- ✦ swarming
- ✦ larva
- ✦ cocoons
- ✦ burrow

Vocabulary Development

Apposition defines a word in the same sentence. Look at the word *burrow*. Look for the use of apposition to find the word's meaning.

Vocabulary
Warm-Up

Autumn is a time of great change in a forest. Take a nature hike through the woods in mid-October. You will see many things changing. Some things change color, some change texture, and some change shape.

Many trees are no longer green. This is the most obvious difference between summer and fall. The leaves are teeming with shades of yellow, orange, and red. Then the leaves shrivel up and fall to the ground. They become brown and brittle. When a strong wind blows, they circulate lightly in the air. Then they fall back to the ground. Each fallen leaf eventually decays.

The forest was once lush and green. The trees were full of leaves and plump fruit. Now many branches are barren. Microbes will decompose the uneaten fruit that falls to the ground. Any remains will enrich the soil for next year's season of growth.

Signs of animal life change. Flies and bees that were swarming all summer seem to disappear. A butterfly larva, called a caterpillar, hides away in one of many cocoons that can be seen hanging from tree branches. Small animals start preparing for a long winter. Squirrels hide acorns, and chipmunks store seeds. A rabbit prepares its burrow, the hole in the ground where it lives.

Soon winter will arrive, but it will end as spring begins. Animals will leave their hiding places, and plants will come to life again. Then summer will return, and autumn will follow closely on its heels.

It is fun to watch the seasons change. And it is good to know the changes will happen again and again.

Vocabulary Word Play

Write one of the words in the diamond. Write examples of the word in the boxes. Have a partner write words that describe the word in the ovals. Then switch roles and create organizers for each word.

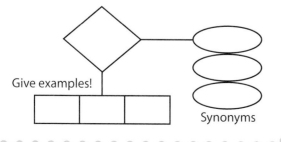

Give examples!

Synonyms

Concept Vocabulary

This lesson's concept word is *recurring. Recurring* means happening over and over. Some things happen only once in a lifetime—like being born. Other events in your life happen over and over again. What are some recurring events in your life? Which ones happen once every year? Which ones happen each day?

CALIFORNIA

READING:
COMPREHENSION AND
ANALYSIS OF GRADE-
LEVEL-APPROPRIATE TEXT 2.6
Distinguish between cause and effect and
between fact and opinion in expository
text. SCIENCE: LIFE SCIENCES 2.c
Students know decomposers, including
many fungi, insects, and microorganisms,
recycle matter from dead plants and
animals.

Genre

Expository Text
tells people something.
It contains facts about real
people, things, or events

Comprehension Skill

☆ **Fact and Opinion**
As you read,
distinguish between
the facts (statements that
can be proved true) and the
opinions (statements about
what someone feels or
thinks is true).

What

Rot!

Nature's Mighty Recycler

by **Elizabeth Ring**

photos by ***Dwight Kuhn***

Focus Questions

What would happen without decomposers? How are decomposers part of food chains and webs?

One day, at a pumpkin patch, you pick a plump pumpkin. You carve a face in its head. You'd like its wide, friendly smile to last forever and ever.

But soon, the pumpkin sags. Now it wears a weird grin.

Before long, spots of mold pop out on the pumpkin's soft head—like blue chicken pox. Your pumpkin's got a bad case of pumpkin rot.

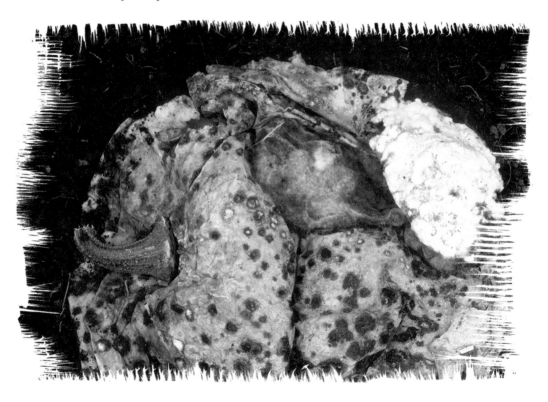

Rot sometimes seems really rotten. It can ruin things you may like a lot—like pumpkins or apples or flowers.

Rot makes a crisp, juicy apple shrivel up and turn brown. It dusts the skin of the apple with white, fuzzy mold.

Rot makes a bright-petaled
daffodil . . .

. . . droop its head and
look sad—

like a small,
burst balloon.

Rot changes
splashy fall leaves . . .

. . . into brittle brown lace.
In the end, the leaves crumble
away. That's okay, though.
That's just nature keeping the
cycle of life rolling by making
things change all the time.

Without rot, leaves and other dead things would pile up,
miles high. They could smother the earth. New plants couldn't
grow. The truth is that without rot the whole world could die.

Rot is a mighty force that never stops moving. It slowly
decays whatever is dying or dead. It weakens the strongest
tree you might climb.

What causes rot? Rotters are mostly animals and plants:
mammals, insects, birds, and especially microbes. To live,
they all need food and shelter—and they find plenty of both
in a dying or dead tree.

Dozens of different kinds of rotters invade a tree as it dies. Some of these rotters, like bacteria, are microbes that are too small to see—except under a microscope. Other microbes, called fungi, also feed on the tree. You can sometimes see fungi fruits, such as mushrooms, when they push out from the tree's bark. Millions of microbes live inside the tree—feeding, growing, spreading, dying, and, all the while, breaking down the tree's wood.

Many kinds of beetles crawl on the tree. Some kinds poke into cracks in the bark, hunting for insects swarming inside the tree. When this click beetle, which eats very little, was a young wireworm (a larva), it lived both in the ground and under the tree's bark.

Other insects poke, scratch, and chew. Small cracks in the bark become holes. Rain, ice, snow, and dew seep under the bark. There, in the dark, microbes thrive and spread. The wood gets softer each day. Woodpeckers and other birds chip away, hunting insects, making nests.

An owl makes its home in a hollow where two branches meet.

A chipmunk digs a burrow at the tree's loosening roots.

All this rotting activity weakens the tree, hour upon hour. Rot reaches into the tree's core, and the dead tree falls to the ground. Now the tree is a log. Kick the log and you splinter the soft wood.

Termites chew at the wood and the log rots away, day after day . . . after day . . . after day.

Hundreds of ants live in tunnels and galleries that they scoop out of the crumbling log. Here a worker ant tends cocoons in an ant nursery.

An ichneumon wasp uses its long tail to drill through the bark and plant its eggs in tunnels other insects have made. When the eggs hatch, the wasp larvae feed on the larvae of the other insects that live in the log.

Fungi, great rotters, grow fast on a log. You sometimes see webs of fungi threads on the bark. Some are white, like a splash of spilled milk. Others look like yellow straw.

Slime mold drapes itself on the log, like a fancy lace collar.

Knobs of lichen stand up stiff and straight.

Some fungi fruits grow big and bloom in odd shapes.

Moss also is a good rotter. Moss plants cover a log like a spongy carpet and sprout little cases full of tiny seedlike grains called spores.

When spores are ripe, they explode—like small fireworks displays. The spores are carried all over, by wind and water, and even in or on animals that may roam far and wide. Some spores will die, but many will settle in places such as damp, rotting logs, where new moss plants can grow.

The day comes when a log—and every other dead thing—become part of the soil. Millions of microbes, insects, earthworms, snails, beetles, and other rotters in the soil continue to eat, grow, multiply, and die—all helping to enrich the soil for new growth.

Hordes of earthworms play a big role in making good soil. As they churn through the dirt, they mix bits of wood, rotten plants, bone, sand, animal droppings (including their own), and much more. The worms' tunneling also makes open spaces for air and water to circulate.

You might think the soil would smell really rotten, with all the dead stuff it holds. But no. It smells—well, earthy, almost sweet. Even before it is fully decayed, the soil feels moist and looks rich.

Every spring, when the sun warms the earth and rain soaks the ground, new life leaps straight out of the old. New green plants spring from the teeming brown soil.

As the plants grow, many animals feed on them.

When a plant dies, an earthworm may pull a leaf, a stem, or a twig underground and eat it when it decays.

Everything eats everything else. This food chain is a big part of the cycle of life. The earthworm may be snatched by a hungry shrew.

The shrew may be caught and eaten by an owl or some other predator. And when that animal dies, its body, too, becomes part of the soil.

When new life grows in a forest, a field, or a garden, it always contains invisible traces of things that gave their lives to the soil. These traces hold nutrients that help new life grow. The cycle of life keeps turning, like a clock that will never stop.

In a way, your pumpkin is going to live on—forever. Last year's pumpkin may seem to be gone. But it's there somewhere. It gave itself to the soil—seeds and all. And the soil is giving it back in new pumpkins.

Meet the Author

Elizabeth Ring

Ring knows a lot about nature! She has written a lot of books about animals, their homes, and how things in nature work. Many of these books have been for the National Wildlife Federation. This group works to protect America's wildlife. Ring also worked as a teacher. For a while, she helped make the children's nature magazine *Ranger Rick.* She lives in Woodbury, Connecticut.

Meet the Photographer

Dwight Kuhn

Getting a close-up photo of an animal can be tricky, but that is what Kuhn is good at. Kuhn learned about biology in college. He worked as a teacher for many years. These days, he is a full-time photographer. Many children's books have Kuhn's photos in them. He has also published magazine photo essays. These are groups of photos that tell stories. Because of his skill, his photos teach while being beautiful.

194

READING: COMPREHENSION AND ANALYSIS OF GRADE-LEVEL-APPROPRIATE TEXT **2.4** Evaluate new information and hypotheses by testing them against known information and ideas. **2.5** Compare and contrast information on the same topic after reading several passages or articles. WRITING: ORGANIZATION AND FOCUS **1.1** Select a focus, an organization structure, and a point of view based upon purpose, audience, length, and format requirements. SCIENCE: LIFE SCIENCES **2.c** Students know decomposers, including many fungi, insects, and microorganisms, recycle matter from dead plants and animals. **3.d** Students know that most microorganisms do not cause disease and that many are beneficial.

CALIFORNIA

Theme Connections

Discuss

Within the Selection

1. How does moss reproduce?

2. How do earthworms help enrich the soil?

Across Selections

3. How does this selection add to what you learned about food chains and webs described in "Who Eats What?"

4. What does rot have to do with energy?

Beyond the Selection

5. Many people have a compost pile in their yard where they toss leaves, rotten leftovers from the fridge, potato peelings, apple cores, etc. Why do you think someone would want a compost pile?

6. How do microorganisms improve your day-to-day life?

Write

Write a brief poem based on one of the photos in the selection.

Read

Find books and magazine articles about how nature recycles itself.

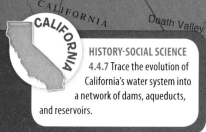

HISTORY-SOCIAL SCIENCE
4.4.7 Trace the evolution of California's water system into a network of dams, aqueducts, and reservoirs.

Social Studies Link

Borrowing Water

Genre

Narrative Nonfiction blends elements of fiction with elements of nonfiction to make a more exciting story.

Text Feature

Maps are a representation, usually on a flat surface, of a region of the earth.

"We learned about climates today in school," Jamie told her dad. "Did you know that, depending on the area, California has many different climates?"

"Really? What is our climate here in southern California?" her father asked.

"It is pretty dry and hot. There are also some deserts. I just can't understand why we haven't run out of water," Jamie said.

"Well, we almost did about one hundred years ago, but now we get our water from other places," her dad replied.

"A long time ago, our region was teeming with streams. People diverted water from these streams for irrigation," he said. "Then artesian wells were used to pump water from underground. But when excessive pumping led to a water shortage, people had to find another source."

"So what did they do?" asked Jamie.

"The City of Los Angeles built an aqueduct that would carry water from the Owens River to the area. As the population grew, there was eventually a large network of dams and aqueducts to water supplies from Northern California and the Colorado River."

"And that's how we get our water today?" Jamie asked.

"It sure is," he answered.

Think Link

1. Look at the map of the Colorado River system. What are some states that might get water from this river?

2. Explain the evolution of California's water supply.

3. How much do you know about the water supply where you live? Do some research to find out more.

WebLink

Visit **www.ImagineItReading.com/ AtHome** for more information about dams, aqueducts, and reservoirs.

Apply

Maps As you work on your investigation, think about a map that you can use to show facts.

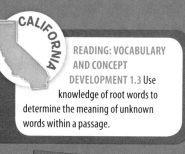

CALIFORNIA

READING: VOCABULARY AND CONCEPT DEVELOPMENT 1.3 Use knowledge of root words to determine the meaning of unknown words within a passage.

Read the story to find the meanings of these words, which are also in "The Great Kapok Tree":

✦ ruins
✦ generations
✦ ancestors
✦ smoldering
✦ clinging
✦ suspended
✦ dangle
✦ wither
✦ pollinate
✦ oxygen
✦ murmured
✦ squawking

Vocabulary Development

Context Clues are hints in the text that help you find meanings of words. Use context clues to find the meanings of *ancestors* and *smoldering*.

Vocabulary

Warm-Up

"This place is really old!" Jacob exclaimed.

Jacob and his grandma were exploring the ruins of an old country schoolhouse behind his grandparents' farm.

"Three generations of my ancestors farmed all the land that you see," his grandma told him proudly, "and my daddy, my granddad, and I all attended this school."

"We'll just peek in—it might be unsafe," his grandma said.

"Look!" Jacob said. "Some of the desks are still here, and there is a wood-burning stove."

"Last summer, I walked back here and found some embers still smoldering in the stove," his grandma said. "Someone must have used the schoolhouse as a campsite or temporary housing."

"Look at all the spider webs clinging to the walls and rafters! There is a spider suspended from that web!" Jacob said.

"I'm not a big fan of spiders," his grandma said, making a face. "I want to show you something." She led Jacob to an open meadow behind the schoolhouse and pointed to a rickety fence.

"I'm too old to sit on that fence and dangle my legs like I used to do," she said. "These legs of mine are starting to wither. But I can still lie on the soft grass and breathe in the sweet smell of wildflowers and watch the bees pollinate them."

Grandma and Jacob found the perfect spot and stretched out on their backs while the sun beamed down on them softly.

"Ahh . . . breathe in that clean oxygen," Jacob murmured as he began to doze off.

Suddenly, a loud squawking sound jolted Jacob out of his slumber. "So much for my nap!" Jacob said, and he and his grandma headed back to the farm.

Vocabulary Word Play

On a separate sheet of paper, work with a partner to organize all the vocabulary words according to their parts of speech. Then share your list with the class.

Concept Vocabulary

This lesson's concept word is *ecosystem.* An *ecosystem* is all the living and nonliving things in a certain area that are linked together. A rain forest is an example of an ecosystem. In a rain forest, you might find spider monkeys, sloths, toucans, poison arrow frogs, fig trees, orchids, and rivers. Think of three other ecosystems. Now choose one of them and think of ten living and nonliving things that are a part of that ecosystem.

CALIFORNIA

READING: STRUCTURAL
FEATURES OF LITERATURE
3.1 Describe the structural
differences of various forms
of literature, including fantasies, fables,
myths, legends, and fairy tales. **SCIENCE:
LIFE SCIENCES 2.b** Students know
producers and consumers (herbivores,
carnivores, omnivores, and decomposers)
are related in food chains and food webs
and may compete with each other for
resources in an ecosystem. **3.c.** Students
know many plants depend on animals for
pollination and seed dispersal, and animals
depend on plants for food and shelter.

Genre

A **fantasy** is an imaginary
story that contains
characters, settings, or
events that are impossible
and do not exist in the
real world.

Comprehension
Skill

☆ **Classify and
Categorize**
As you read, put
like things together to
understand the
relationships set up by
the author.

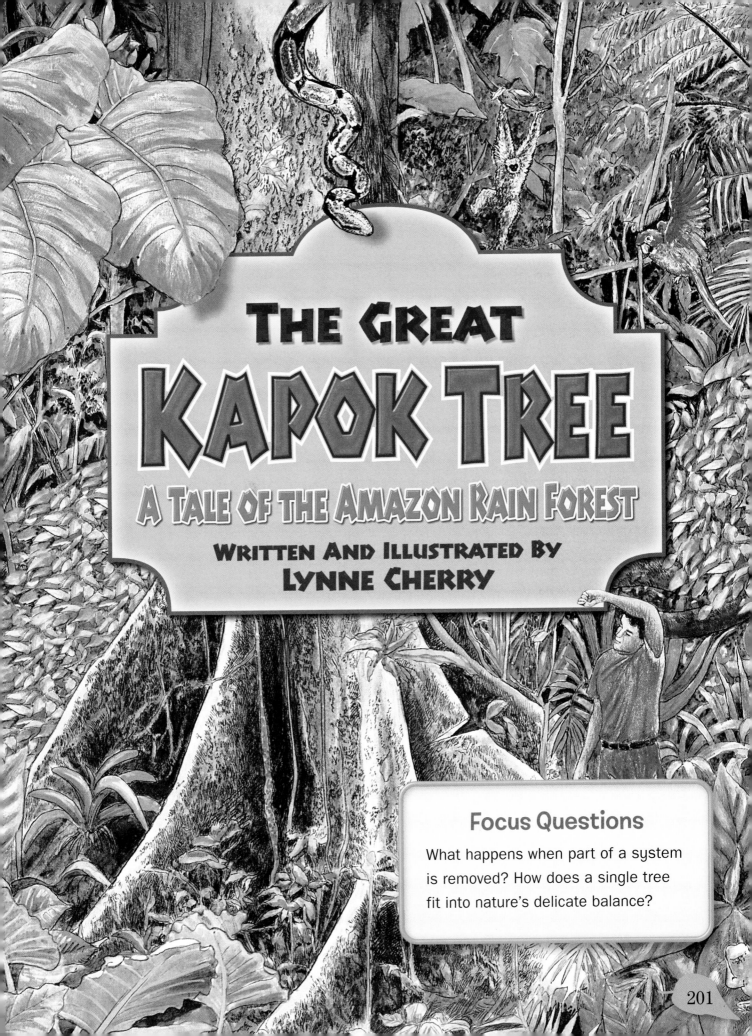

The Great

KAPOK TREE

A Tale of the Amazon Rain Forest

Written And Illustrated By
Lynne Cherry

Focus Questions

What happens when part of a system is removed? How does a single tree fit into nature's delicate balance?

Two men walked into the rain forest. Moments before, the forest had been alive with the sounds of squawking birds and howling monkeys. Now all was quiet as the creatures watched the two men and wondered why they had come.

The larger man stopped and pointed to a great Kapok tree. Then he left.

The smaller man took the ax he carried and struck the trunk of the tree. Whack! Whack! Whack! The sounds of the blows rang through the forest. The wood of the tree was very hard. Chop! Chop! Chop! The man wiped off the sweat that ran down his face and neck. Whack! Chop! Whack! Chop!

Soon the man grew tired. He sat down to rest at the foot of the great Kapok tree. Before he knew it, the heat and hum of the forest had lulled him to sleep.

A boa constrictor lived in the Kapok tree. He slithered down its trunk to where the man was sleeping. He looked at the gash the ax had made in the tree. Then the huge snake slid very close to the man and hissed in his ear: "Senhor, this tree is a tree of miracles. It is my home, where generations of my ancestors have lived. Do not chop it down."

202

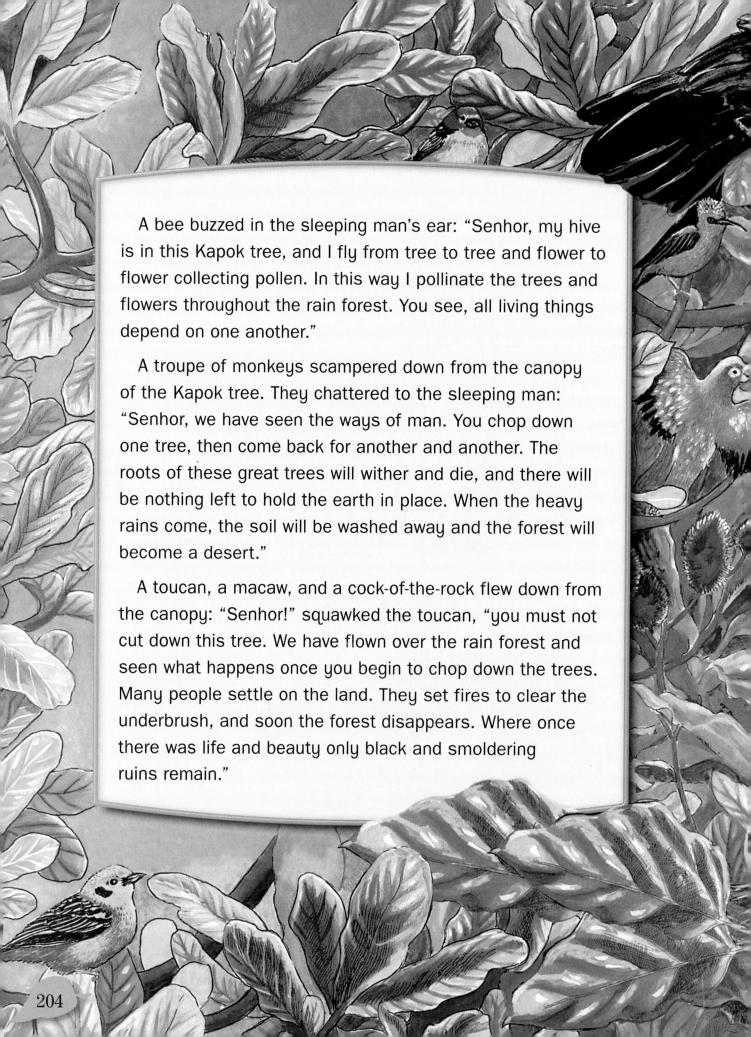

A bee buzzed in the sleeping man's ear: "Senhor, my hive is in this Kapok tree, and I fly from tree to tree and flower to flower collecting pollen. In this way I pollinate the trees and flowers throughout the rain forest. You see, all living things depend on one another."

A troupe of monkeys scampered down from the canopy of the Kapok tree. They chattered to the sleeping man: "Senhor, we have seen the ways of man. You chop down one tree, then come back for another and another. The roots of these great trees will wither and die, and there will be nothing left to hold the earth in place. When the heavy rains come, the soil will be washed away and the forest will become a desert."

A toucan, a macaw, and a cock-of-the-rock flew down from the canopy: "Senhor!" squawked the toucan, "you must not cut down this tree. We have flown over the rain forest and seen what happens once you begin to chop down the trees. Many people settle on the land. They set fires to clear the underbrush, and soon the forest disappears. Where once there was life and beauty only black and smoldering ruins remain."

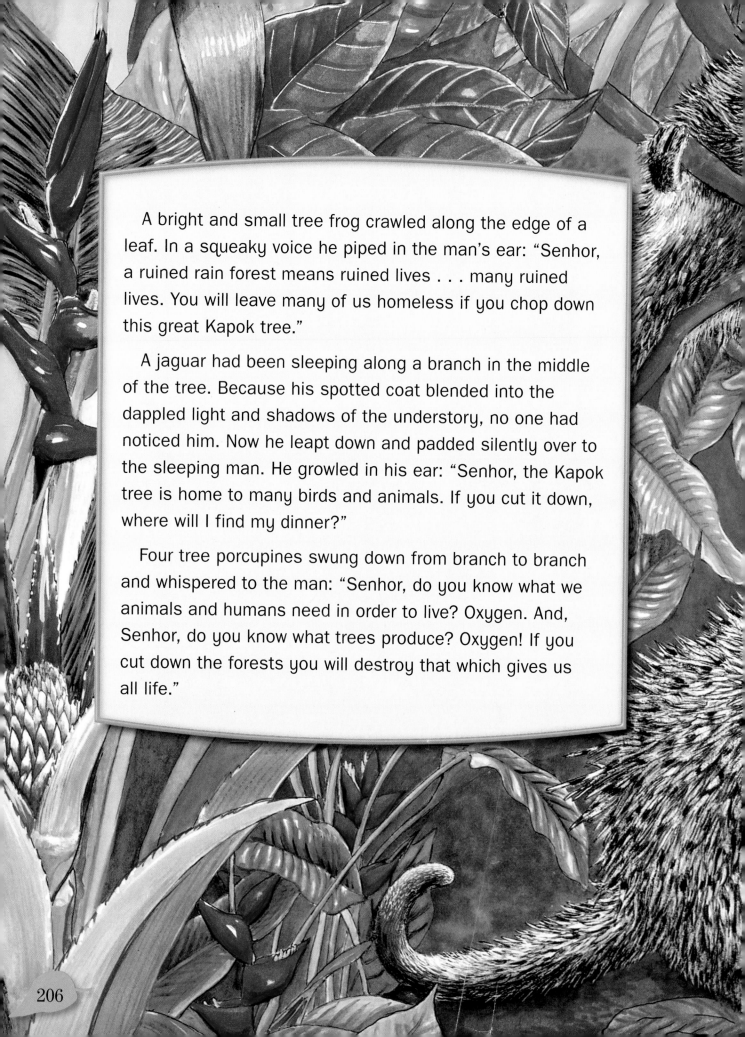

A bright and small tree frog crawled along the edge of a leaf. In a squeaky voice he piped in the man's ear: "Senhor, a ruined rain forest means ruined lives . . . many ruined lives. You will leave many of us homeless if you chop down this great Kapok tree."

A jaguar had been sleeping along a branch in the middle of the tree. Because his spotted coat blended into the dappled light and shadows of the understory, no one had noticed him. Now he leapt down and padded silently over to the sleeping man. He growled in his ear: "Senhor, the Kapok tree is home to many birds and animals. If you cut it down, where will I find my dinner?"

Four tree porcupines swung down from branch to branch and whispered to the man: "Senhor, do you know what we animals and humans need in order to live? Oxygen. And, Senhor, do you know what trees produce? Oxygen! If you cut down the forests you will destroy that which gives us all life."

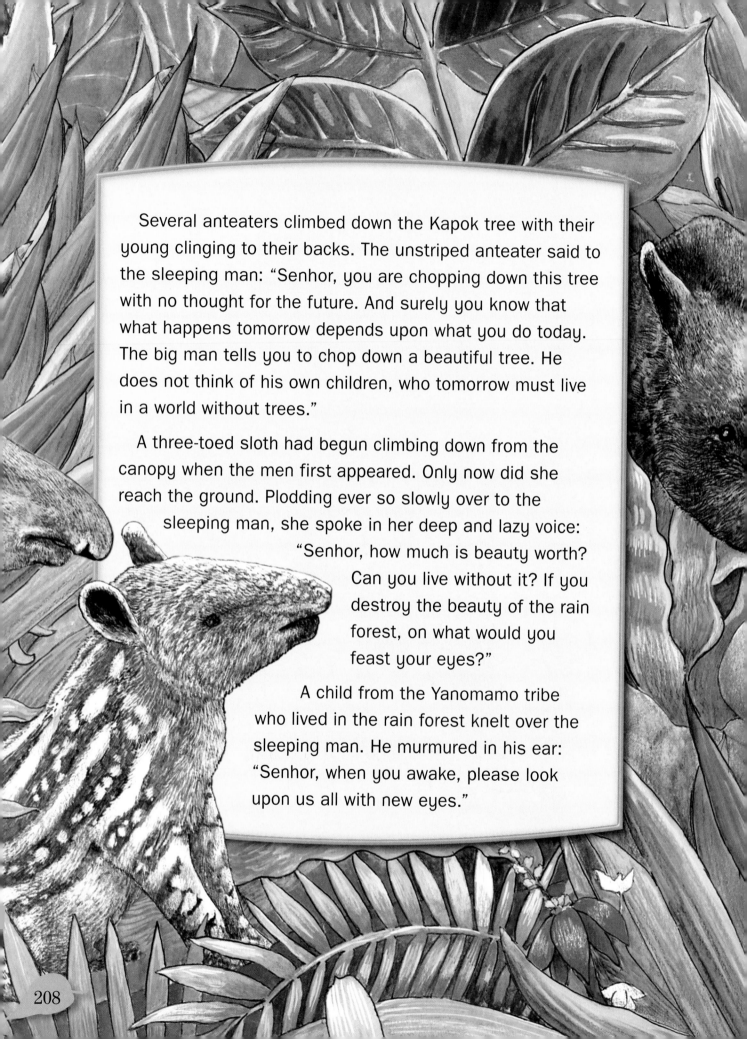

Several anteaters climbed down the Kapok tree with their young clinging to their backs. The unstriped anteater said to the sleeping man: "Senhor, you are chopping down this tree with no thought for the future. And surely you know that what happens tomorrow depends upon what you do today. The big man tells you to chop down a beautiful tree. He does not think of his own children, who tomorrow must live in a world without trees."

A three-toed sloth had begun climbing down from the canopy when the men first appeared. Only now did she reach the ground. Plodding ever so slowly over to the sleeping man, she spoke in her deep and lazy voice: "Senhor, how much is beauty worth? Can you live without it? If you destroy the beauty of the rain forest, on what would you feast your eyes?"

A child from the Yanomamo tribe who lived in the rain forest knelt over the sleeping man. He murmured in his ear: "Senhor, when you awake, please look upon us all with new eyes."

The man awoke with a start. Before him stood the rain forest child, and all around him, staring, were the creatures who depended upon the great Kapok tree. What wondrous and rare animals they were!

211

The man looked about and saw the sun streaming through the canopy. Spots of bright light glowed like jewels amidst the dark green forest. Strange and beautiful plants seemed to dangle in the air, suspended from the great Kapok tree.

The man smelled the fragrant perfume of their flowers. He felt the steamy mist rising from the forest floor. But he heard no sound, for the creatures were strangely silent.

The man stood and picked up his ax. He swung back his arm as though to strike the tree. Suddenly he stopped. He turned and looked at the animals and the child.

He hesitated. Then he dropped the ax and walked out of the rain forest.

Meet the Author and Illustrator

Lynne Cherry

Cherry wants to get children excited about the natural world. When planning her books, she ponders problems children should know about. She thinks about how children can help. Cherry likes to go to schools and talk about nature. She started a group that helps show teachers how nature can be a part of everything at school. When she wants to relax, Cherry hikes and canoes through the world she loves so much.

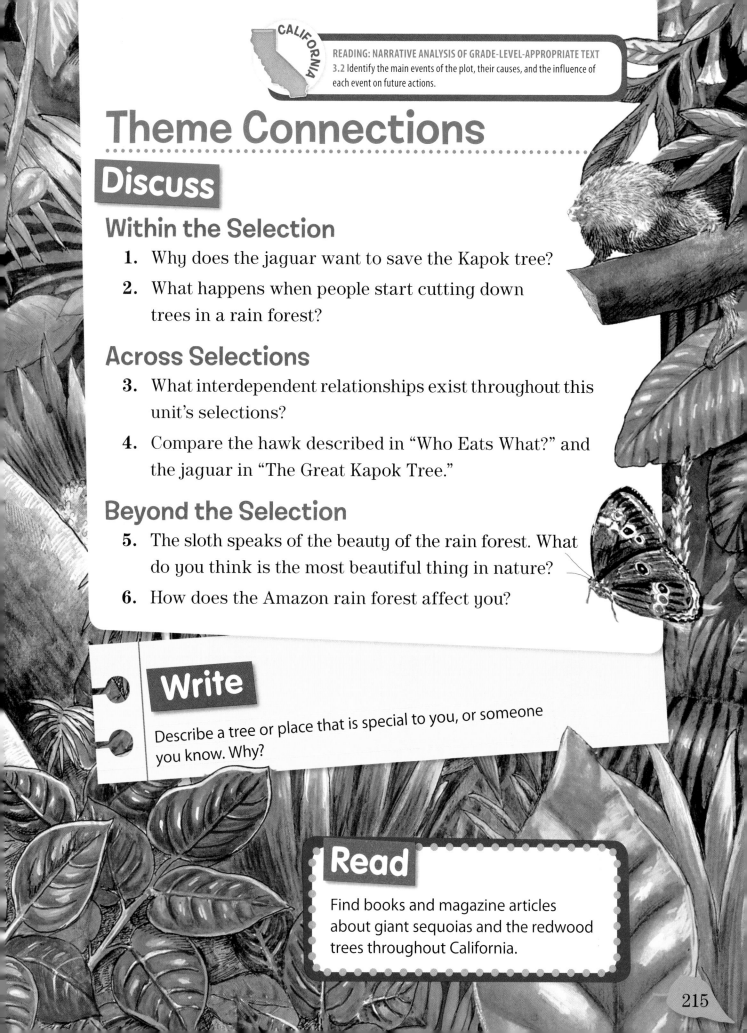

CALIFORNIA

READING: NARRATIVE ANALYSIS OF GRADE-LEVEL-APPROPRIATE TEXT
3.2 Identify the main events of the plot, their causes, and the influence of each event on future actions.

Theme Connections

Discuss

Within the Selection

1. Why does the jaguar want to save the Kapok tree?

2. What happens when people start cutting down trees in a rain forest?

Across Selections

3. What interdependent relationships exist throughout this unit's selections?

4. Compare the hawk described in "Who Eats What?" and the jaguar in "The Great Kapok Tree."

Beyond the Selection

5. The sloth speaks of the beauty of the rain forest. What do you think is the most beautiful thing in nature?

6. How does the Amazon rain forest affect you?

Write

Describe a tree or place that is special to you, or someone you know. Why?

Read

Find books and magazine articles about giant sequoias and the redwood trees throughout California.

CALIFORNIA

SCIENCE: LIFE SCIENCES
3.a. Students know ecosystems can be characterized by their living and nonliving components.

Science Link

THE SACRAMENTO RIVER

Genre

Expository Text tells people something. It contains facts about real people, things, or events.

Text Feature

Charts present information in an organized and visual way.

The Sacramento River is the longest river in California. Artificial channels make it easy for boats to travel. Ships can come in from the ocean to deliver cargo.

In 1849, California experienced a gold rush. Many people came to California in search of fortune. Some of our ancestors panned for gold in the river. They used a heavy metal called mercury to find the gold. Gold stuck to the mercury. After a while, however, the gold became harder to find in the streams. Miners began looking for gold in the rocks instead.

Cottonwood branches dangle into the water. The shaded sunlight makes the banks of the Sacramento River look almost dappled. The shade helps cool the water for trout that swim deep and provides cover for salmon. The salmon lay their eggs in "spawning gravel." Sand and gravel bars provide a place for birds to nest and feed. Otters, beavers, and turtles live along the river's edge, as do frogs and snakes.

The riparian forests are along the Sacramento River. They provide habitat for more than 250 kinds of animals. Lots of birds migrate through the forest. Tall oak trees grow farther away from the water. Walnuts, prunes, and alfalfa grow in the rich soil that was once flooded by the river. Most of the world's prune and walnut supply grows in this area.

Many people live in cities and towns near the Sacramento River. The river is important to their economy. The river provides water for farms in the nearby valley too. Some of the farmers are planting native trees and shrubs to help improve the ecosystem.

Think Link

1. On a sheet of paper, create a two-column chart that lists things that can be found in or near the Sacramento River. In one column, list five nonliving things. In the other column, list five living things.

2. Why do you think the artificial channels make it easier for boats to travel?

3. Many birds migrate through the riparian forests. Where do you think they are going? Why do you think they migrate through these forests? Explain your answers.

CALIFORNIA WebLink

Visit **www.ImagineItReading.com/ AtHome** for more information about the Sacramento River and other watershed areas.

Apply

Charts As you work on your investigation, think about how charts can present information in an organized and visual way.

Circle of Songs

by
Cynthia Porter

The flowers sing a song of earth;

bees sing a song of flowers.

The wind that sings across the sky

sings of sun and showers.

The sun sings songs of shining light;

the round earth sings of spinning.

Birds sing a song of bright blue sky,

and spring sings of beginning.

Focus Question How are nature's various cycles linked?

Yellow Leaf

by Fredrick Zydek

A single yellow leaf
slips from a tree,
wafts its gentle way
to the stream below.

Yellow leaf, how do I
draw you near?
Shall I use the rain
hissing on the pines,

the lashes of ferns
and lilies, a short
stick? How shall I
ever make you mine?

Shall I wade out
to my knees, face
the wilds of the watery
deep that sweeps you
down the mountains
to the waiting sea,
the yellow sands
of the waiting sea?

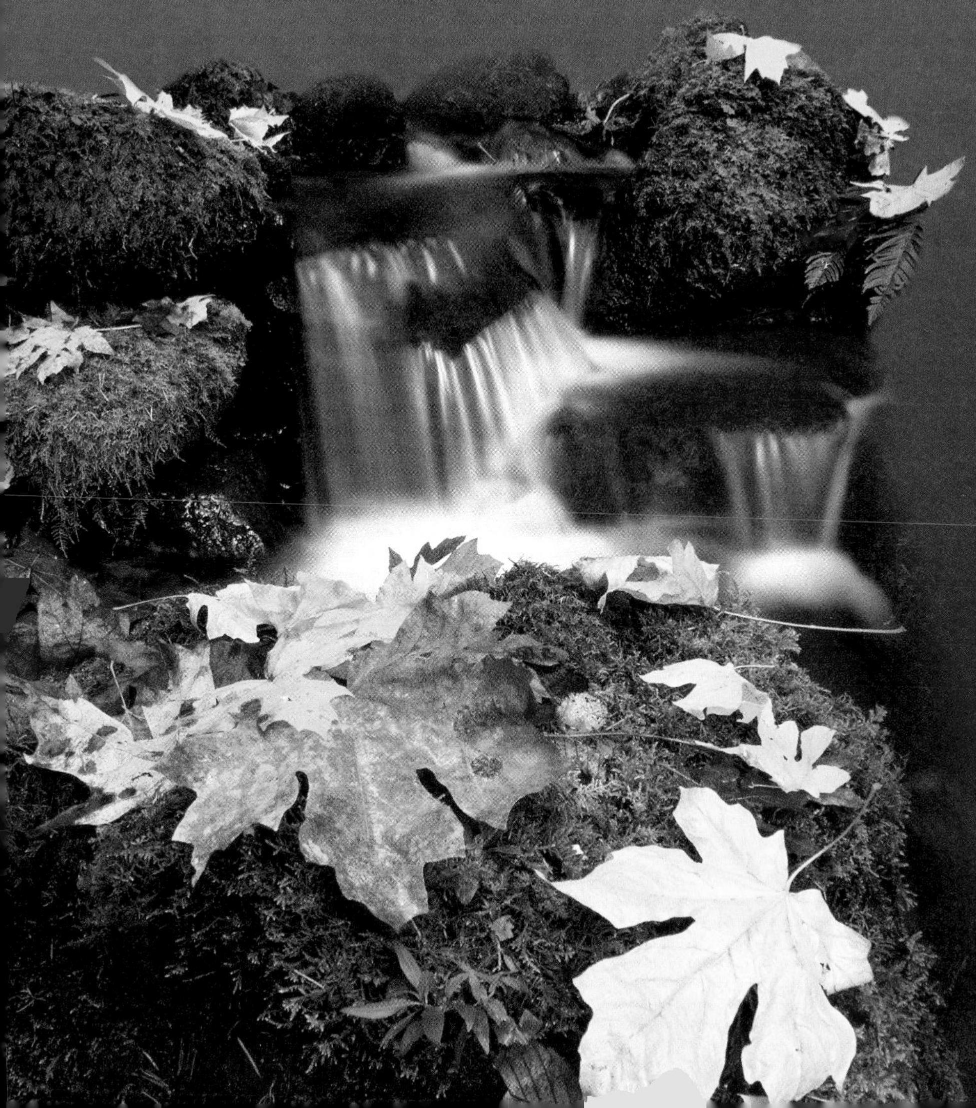

MOLD, MOLD

by Jack Prelutsky

Mold, mold,
marvelous mold,
alluring to look at,
enthralling to hold,
you are so delightful
I can't help but smile
when I nuzzle a smidgen
of mold for awhile.

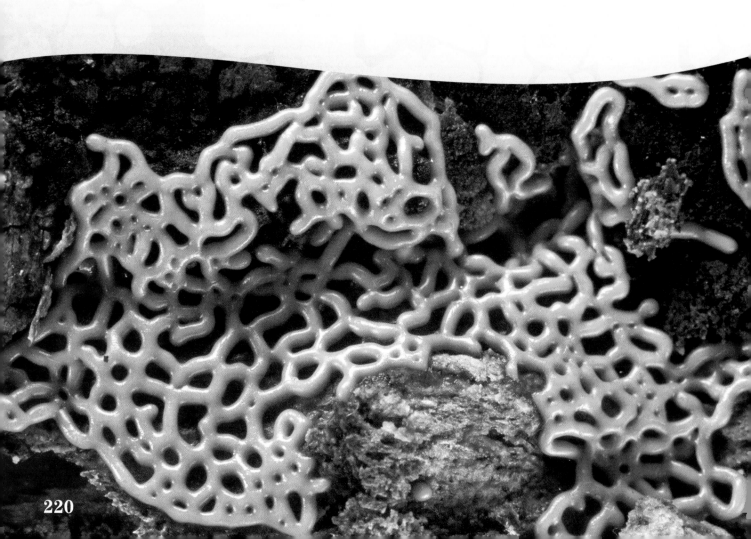

Slime, slime,
savory slime,
you're luscious and succulent
any old time,
there's hardly a thing
that is nearly as grand
as a dollop of slime
in the palm of my hand.

Some think you are miserable
manners of muck,
they can't stand to see you,
you make them say, "Yuck!"
But I think you're fetching,
beguiling and fine,
mold, you are glorious,
slime, you're divine.

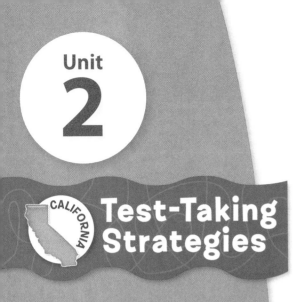

Test-Taking Strategy: Identifying and Using Important Words

Pay attention to important words in directions and questions. These important words will help you find the correct answer.

Identifying and Using Important Words

All questions and answer choices have important words. When you read questions and answer choices, try to find the important words. They will help you answer the question correctly.

Read the sample problem below. Think about the important words in the question and answer choices.

1. According to this article, what should you do with a garden in the fall?

    A   use less water

    B   use more fertilizer

    C   pull all the plants out of the ground

    D   cover the plants with plastic

The important words in the question are *According to this article* and *fall*. The words *According to this article* tell you that you should use the information in the article, not other information that you might have heard or read. The word *fall* tells you the time of year you should think about.

In some questions, the important words can include *less*, *more*, and *all*. These words, even the small ones, help you understand the question and the answer choices. It is important that you carefully read every word in the question and the answer choices.

Test-Taking Practice

**Read the following rough draft of a student's report.
It contains errors. Then answer Numbers 1 through 6.**

1 Every day, tons of trash end up in America's landfills. Almost one-third of the trash is kitchen and yard waste. To reduce this mountain of trash, many people use composting. This helps piles of waste decay naturally.

2 Compost is made by billions of microbes. Microbes are tiny living things such as fungi and bakteria. They eat and digest waste. In short, they turn trash into compost. Compost is a dark, crumbly form of soil. The soil is added to gardens to make plants grow better.

3 The best microbes are aerobic, which means that they need air to work. If there is not enough air, anaerobic microbes take over. Anaerobic microbes do not need air, and they decompose trash more slowly. In addition, they smell bad. To limit anaerobic microbes in compost piles, people lift and turn the waste with a garden fork or spale. Turning the compost keeps it from sticking together. Adding straw can help create more space for air too.

4 Every piece of waste needs a thin coating of water so microbes can live. If the compost pile is too dry, few microbes can live there. The garbage will take longer to decay. If there is too much water, the waste gets soggy and clumps together. In wet areas, compost piles must be covered to keep them from getting too damp. In dry areas, a compost pile must be watered regularly.

5 Finally, microbes need two major kinds of food: browns and greens. Browns are dry, dead plants such as sawdust, dead weeds, straw, and leaves that have fallen from the trees. Browns also are important because they make air pockets in the compost pile.

6 Greens are leaves, grass, or plants. Some things that are not green in color are still considered greens. Coffee grounds, tea bags, and manure are greens. Greens have nitrogen, which microbes need to grow. They also supply microbes with water. Mixing browns and greens gives microbes air, moisture, and food.

Use what you learned from the report to answer Numbers 1 through 6. Write your answers on a piece of paper.

1. Read this sentence from Paragraph 2.

> Microbes are tiny living things such as fungi and <u>bakteria</u>.

Which is the correct way to spell the underlined word?

A bacteeria

B bacteria

C bakteeria

D Leave as is.

2. Read this sentence from Paragraph 1.

> To reduce this mountain <u>of trash, many people</u> use composting.

Which is the correct way to write the underlined part of the sentence?

A of trash many, people

B of trash many people

C of trash, many people

D Leave as is.

3. Read this sentence from Paragraph 3.

> To limit anaerobic microbes in compost piles, people lift and turn the waste with a garden fork or <u>spale</u>.

What should the underlined word be?

A spake

B spane

C spade

D Leave as is.

Test Tips

- Skim the questions, and do the easiest ones first.

- Think about the question.

- Look at each answer choice.

4. Read this sentence from Paragraph 6.

> Coffee <u>grounds</u>, <u>tea</u> <u>bags</u>, and manure are greens.

Which underlined words should be capitalized?

A grounds

B tea

C bags

D Leave as is.

5. Which sentence could *best* be added to the end of Paragraph 6?

A All three are necessary to turn waste into compost.

B Mixing is very important.

C Browns and greens are vital to science.

D Nitrogen helps microbes grow.

6. Which of the following statements from the article is an opinion?

A Anaerobic microbes do not need air.

B Compost is made by microbes.

C Anaerobic microbes smell bad.

D Compost microbes need water.

A Changing State

From the Native Americans who first populated its woods to the Spanish explorers who colonized its coastline and from the Gold Rush to the rise of Hollywood, the state of California is rich with history. California's spirit of discovery and adventure is enduring—one that continues to reveal itself in new, surprising ways. How much do you know about your state? How did the state and its people change as it grew?

Fine Art
Theme Connection

Look at the painting.

- What famous California location has the artist captured?

- What details can you locate in this painting?

- What does this painting "say" about California?

Albert Bierstadt (1830–1902)
Valley of the Yosemite. 1864.
Oil on canvas.

BIG Idea

How has California changed over time?

CALIFORNIA

READING: VOCABULARY AND CONCEPT DEVELOPMENT 1.3 Use knowledge of root words to determine the meaning of unknown words within a passage.

Read the story to find the meanings of these words, which are also in "The First Californians":

✦ isolated
✦ dispute
✦ presidios
✦ domain
✦ mortar
✦ epidemics
✦ ceded
✦ peninsula
✦ missionaries
✦ paleontologists
✦ submerged
✦ fossilized

Vocabulary Development

Context Clues are hints in the text that help you find the meanings of words. Look at the words *domain* and *paleontologists*. Use context clues to find each word's meaning.

Vocabulary

Warm-Up

Corrine and Alanna looked out at the San Francisco Bay. The morning sun was bright, and the surf crashed loudly against the rocks. Their teacher, Mr. Andrews, instructed the class to behave.

"Field trips are special," Mr. Andrews told them. "If you get out of line, you'll be isolated from the class!"

"I won't dispute that," Corrine whispered to Alanna.

The tour guide introduced himself as Simon. He was tall, had a long white beard, and wore a park ranger uniform.

"Presidios used to be the domain of Spain," Simon gestured to the brick-and-mortar buildings around them.

"That rhymes!" Alanna giggled.

"In 1776, the Spanish arrived here and built The Presidio," Simon continued. "Through war and epidemics, it stood. Spain eventually ceded control to the U.S. It was perfect for an outpost."

"Why?" Corrine asked.

"We're on a peninsula," Simon told them. "Water is on three sides. Missionaries and soldiers found it easy to come and go."

The class followed Simon along the shore.

"Paleontologists have scoured this land," Simon said. "Millions of years ago, this was all submerged under water."

"Have you found any dinosaur fossils?" Alanna asked.

"No," he laughed. "Their fossilized remains are not in the Bay."

Corrine and Alanna started to wander away from the rest of the class, but Mr. Andrews quickly found them.

"The Presidio has already been explored, girls," he said. "If you don't catch up with the class, the only thing you're going to discover is trouble!"

Vocabulary Word Play

On a separate sheet of paper, work with a partner to create a short paragraph using the vocabulary words. Then share your paragraph with the class.

Concept Vocabulary

This lesson's concept word is *exploration*. *Exploration* refers to the investigation of unexplored regions and territories. Think about what it was like to discover new land, new people, and new opportunities. Think of as many different kinds of exploration as possible. Write them down, and share them with a classmate.

READING: VOCABULARY AND CONCEPT DEVELOPMENT 1.2 Apply knowledge of word origins, derivations, synonyms, antonyms, and idioms to determine the meaning of words and phrases. HISTORY-SOCIAL SCIENCE 4.2.3 Describe the Spanish exploration of California.

Genre

Expository Text tells people something. It contains facts about real people, things, or events.

Comprehension Skill

☆ **Compare and Contrast**

As you read, compare and contrast thoughts, ideas, and things presented in the text to help you understand the selection.

The First

Californians

by Ann Heinrichs

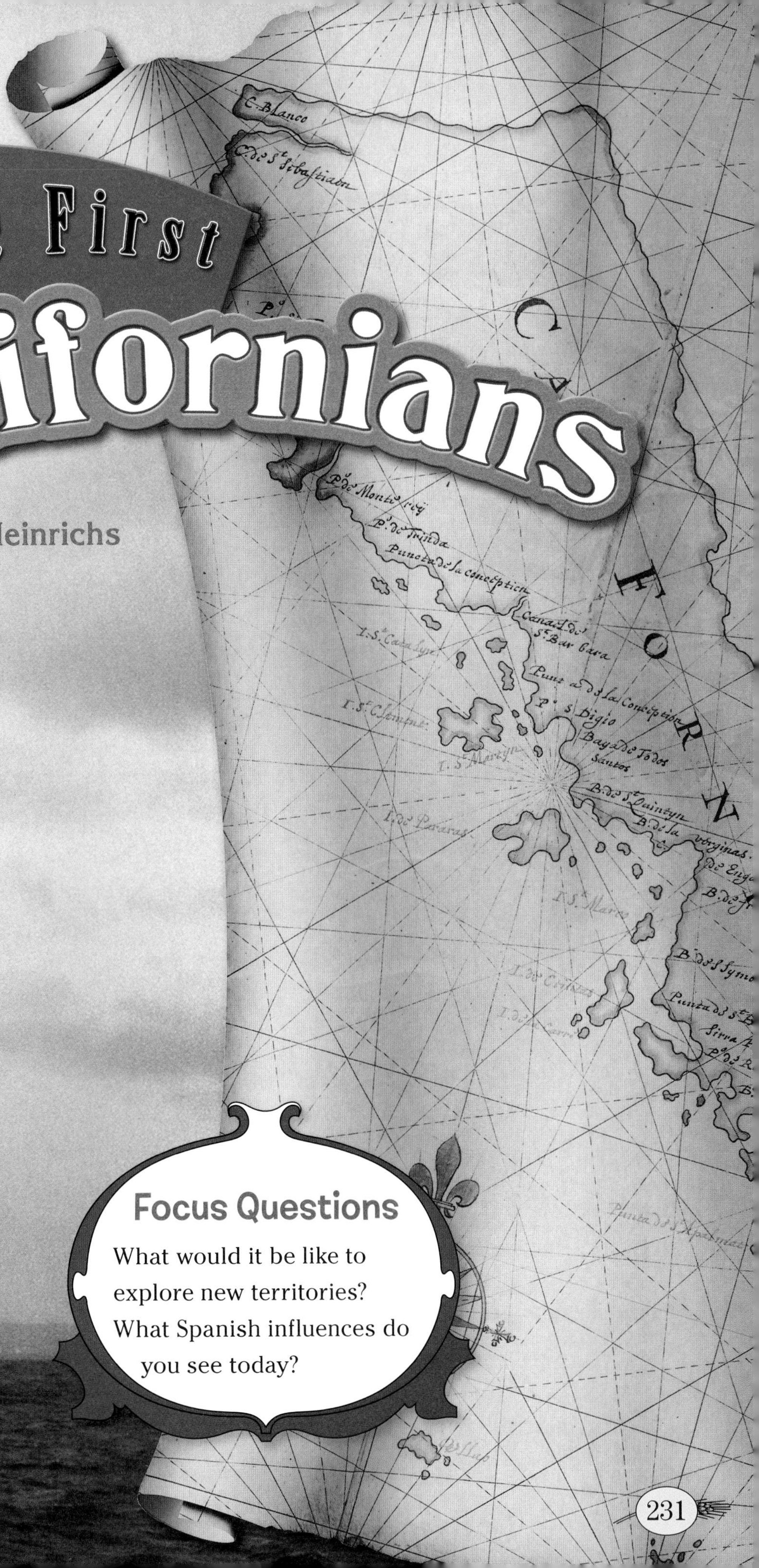

Focus Questions

What would it be like to explore new territories? What Spanish influences do you see today?

Far across the ocean from Spain lay a fabulous island, a tropical paradise full of griffins and gold. It was California, the domain of Queen Calafía and her lost tribe of Amazons. Spaniards knew of this land from the romantic novel *The Adventures of Esplandián,* by Garci Rodríguez de Montalvo (1510).

When Spanish explorers came upon the peninsula of western Mexico, they were sure they had discovered that fantasy island. They named it California. Only later did they learn it was not an island at all but just a finger off the mainland to the north. So they called the narrow peninsula Baja California (Lower California) and the northern region Alta California (Upper California).

The First Californians

Of course, the Spaniards were latecomers to a land that others had discovered long before. Perhaps 15,000 years earlier, Asian people had crossed a land bridge from present-day Siberia to North America. That bridge is now submerged beneath Alaska's Bering Strait. The people spread south and east to inhabit what is now North and South America. Those in California were isolated by high mountains.

La Brea Tar Pits

About 35,000 years ago, where Los Angeles is now, oil began oozing up to the Earth's surface. Mixed with oxygen, it thickened into gummy black tar. Rainwater collected on top of the tar, and when animals came to drink, their feet got caught in the tar. There they stuck until they died.

Thousands of years later, the bodies were completely covered over with tar. Indians used the tar to waterproof their boats, and settlers used it on their roofs. In 1906, a geologist discovered the fossilized animal bones. It was the largest collection of Pleistocene-era animals ever found.

In Hancock Park, Los Angeles, life-size replicas of the prehistoric victims re-create the scene. Reconstructed skeletons from the tar pits are displayed at the George C. Page Museum of La Brea Discoveries. They include mastodons, mammoths, saber-toothed cats, and a human female. Even today, almost a century after the discovery, paleontologists are still finding, cleaning, and classifying fossils from the tar pits.

A life-size model of an Imperial mammoth stuck in La Brea Tar Pits.

Native Ways of Life

California's Indians lived in clans, or groups of related families. Among the many groups, more than 100 different languages were spoken. The shaman of a tribe was both a spiritual leader and a doctor.

For food, they fished, hunted bear and other wild game, and gathered herbs, roots, nuts, seeds, and berries. In regions where Western pines grew, they ate piñon nuts. Where there were oak trees, acorns were a staple food. Using a stone mortar, the Indians pounded them into meal and added water to make an acorn mush. Then they dropped hot stones into the mush until it was cooked.

A Paiute woman working with a woven winnowing tray.

People in northern and central California wove intricate baskets to carry and store food and valuables, sift acorn meal, serve food, hold water, and cook. Mothers carried their babies on their backs in woven cradle baskets. Caps and moccasins were also woven of plant fibers. People who lived near the coast used shells as money.

The Spanish Period

In 1521, Hernán Cortés conquered Mexico and named it New Spain. He traveled to Baja California in 1534 but did not venture into present-day California. Juan Rodríguez Cabrillo, a Portuguese explorer working for Spain, was the first European to sight what is now the state of California. He sailed into San Diego Bay in 1542. It was Cabrillo who first called this land by the name California.

Spanish explorer Hernán Cortés

English navigator Francis Drake

In 1579, the English navigator Francis Drake cruised along the California coast. At Drake's Bay in present-day Marin County, he landed and met with Miwok Indians. According to Drake, they lived in earth-covered houses that were "very warme" and used woven reed bowls. Drake named this land "New Albion" before sailing on. ("Albion" was a poetic nickname for England.)

On a voyage in 1602, Sebastián Vizcaíno landed at several spots and gave them names. Some of these places were San Diego, San Clemente, Catalina Island, Santa Barbara, Carmel, and Monterey.

Missions and Presidios

Gaspar de Portolá, the Spanish governor of Baja California, enlisted Franciscan friar Junípero Serra to build missions in the new territory. In 1769, Serra opened his first mission—San Diego de Alcalá in present-day San Diego. Near many of the missions, Portolá set up presidios, or military forts. San Diego's presidio opened in 1769 and Monterey's in 1770. A presidio and Mission Dolores marked the founding of San Francisco in 1776.

At Portolá's direction, other missionaries opened more missions up the coast. By 1823, a string of twenty-one missions stretched from San Diego up to Sonoma. Many were about a day's journey apart. The padres (fathers) taught the Indians Christianity, farming, and crafts. With Indian labor, they built churches and operated vast farms and ranches. Captivity, forced labor, and European diseases were a bitter pill for the Indians, though. Runaways and Indian uprisings were common.

Father Junípero Serra

In 1812, Russian fur traders set up Fort Ross on California's northwest coast. The Russian settlement made Spanish officials nervous. Nevertheless, it thrived on hunting sea otters for twenty years.

The Mexican Period

Mexico won its freedom from Spain in 1821, but the new nation practically ignored California. Mexican officials governed the territory, but the presidios were weak and ineffective. The Monterey presidio had three guns but hardly any gunpowder. San Francisco's presidio had ten rusty guns but no soldiers to fire them.

The new Mexican government disbanded California's missions and gave the land to private farmers and ranchers. Many of these estates went to the *Californios*—Mexican merchants and soldiers. They turned their land grants into huge ranchos—a name used for farms as well as ranches.

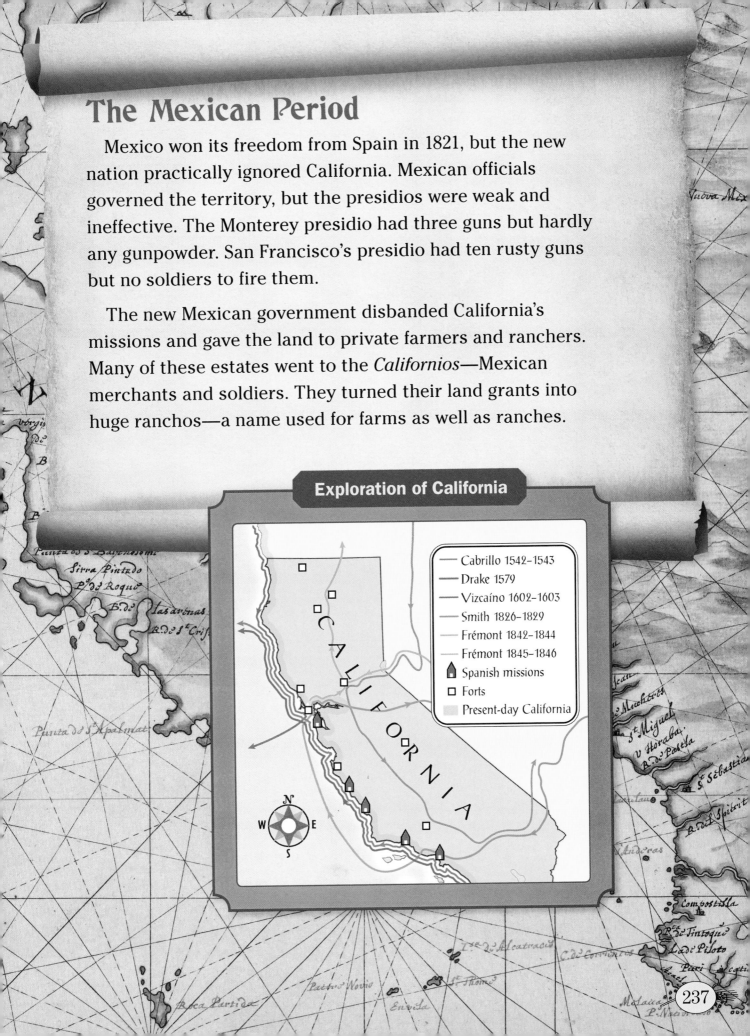

Exploration of California

Cabrillo 1542–1543
Drake 1579
Vizcaíno 1602–1603
Smith 1826–1829
Frémont 1842–1844
Frémont 1845–1846
Spanish missions
Forts
Present-day California

John C. Frémont

Explorer John Charles Frémont (1813–1890) led the U.S. government's first overland expedition into California in the 1840s. He helped win California from Mexico in the Mexican War and served as one of California's first two U.S. senators (1850–1851). Frémont later became the nation's first Republican presidential candidate (1856) but lost to James Buchanan.

Then began the great westward migration of settlers from the United States. Jedediah Smith was the first to arrive overland. He trudged across the Mojave Desert in 1826 and became the first white man to cross the Sierra Nevada mountain range. The first of many wagon trains to California left Missouri in 1841. Many travelers died in cholera epidemics or Indian attacks. The fate of the Donner party was especially tragic. Of the eighty-seven men, women, and children in the party, almost half starved or froze to death in the Sierra Nevada.

Most of the new settlers were just small-scale farmers or shopkeepers. But some began to be powerful merchants and government officials. Soon, not even the Californios expected that Mexico could hang on to California much longer. One "troublemaker" was John C. Frémont, a U.S. Army surveyor. He defied Mexican officials by raising the American flag near Monterey.

The Bear Flag Revolt

Texas was another territory that belonged to Mexico at this time. As in California, more and more American settlers had been moving in. Yankees in Texas finally fought Mexico and won their independence in 1836. That gave Californians the idea to take over their territory, too.

In June 1846, a handful of settlers in Sonoma stitched together a crude flag showing a bear and a star. Up went the flag as they declared the California Republic, with William B. Ide as president. This incident became known as the Bear Flag Revolt.

During the Bear Flag Revolt of 1846, a group of settlers seized the town of Sonoma, raised the Bear Flag, and proclaimed the California Republic.

In July, a U.S. Navy fleet sailed into San Francisco Bay. Commodore John Sloat raised the American flag, declaring California a U.S. territory. The bold new California Republic had lasted only a month.

Meanwhile, Texas had become a U.S. state. In the dispute over its boundaries, the Mexican-American War broke out. It ended with a U.S. victory. On February 2, 1848, the two nations drew up the terms of their agreement in the Treaty of Guadalupe Hidalgo. Mexico ceded about half of its entire territory—including California—to the United States.

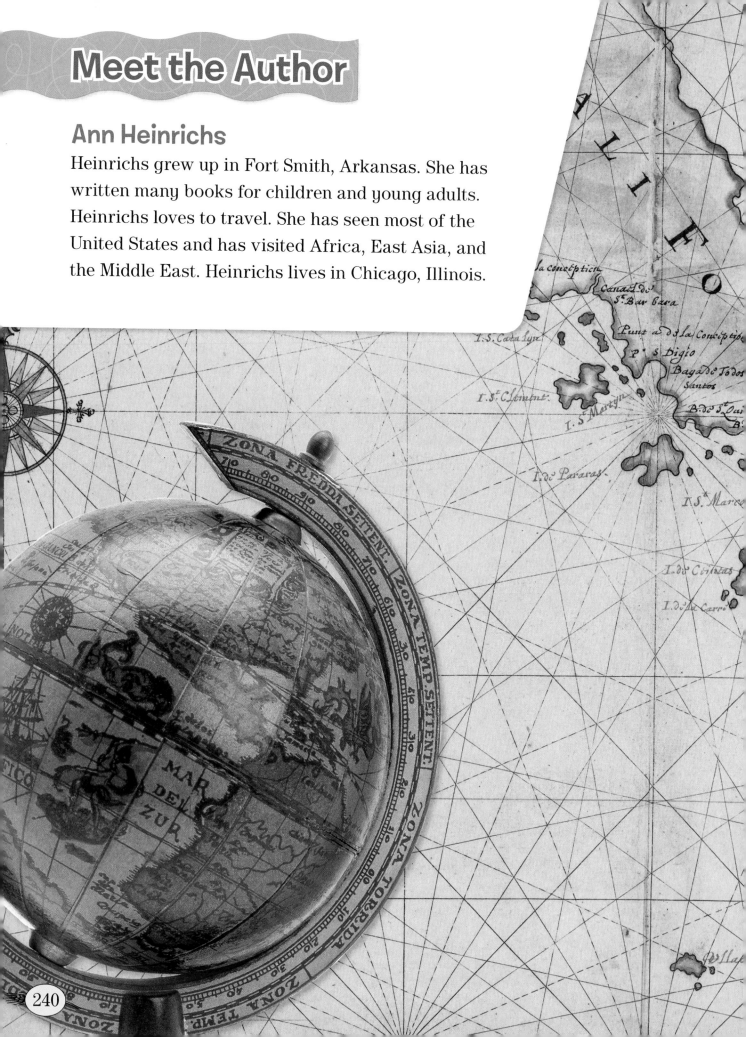

Meet the Author

Ann Heinrichs

Heinrichs grew up in Fort Smith, Arkansas. She has written many books for children and young adults. Heinrichs loves to travel. She has seen most of the United States and has visited Africa, East Asia, and the Middle East. Heinrichs lives in Chicago, Illinois.

HISTORY-SOCIAL SCIENCE 4.2.3 Describe the Spanish exploration and colonization of California, including the relationships among soldiers, missionaries, and Indians **4.2.4** Describe the mapping of, geographic basis of, and economic factors in the placement and function of the Spanish missions.

Theme Connections

Discuss

Within the Selection

1. How does the selection reflect the unit theme, A Changing State?

2. What sorts of influences, positive and negative, did Spanish explorers have on the native peoples of California?

Beyond the Selection

3. What influences or contributions from the first Californians can you still see today?

4. Would you be interested in exploring uncharted lands and finding new civilizations?

Write

Write about a time when you felt adventurous.

Read

Find magazine or newspaper articles that discuss changes in the town or city where you live in California.

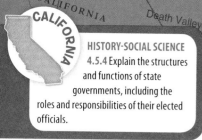

CALIFORNIA

HISTORY-SOCIAL SCIENCE
4.5.4 Explain the structures and functions of state governments, including the roles and responsibilities of their elected officials.

Social Studies Link

State Governments

Created for the original thirteen colonies, the U.S. Constitution is the law of our land. Did you know that each state also has a constitution?

This system of having state and national governments is called federalism. We often call the U.S. government the federal government. Like the national government, each state government has three branches: executive, legislative, and judicial.

A state's executive branch is headed by a governor. The governor signs bills that become laws. A state's legislative branch is made up of a Senate and a House of Representatives. Some states call the House the Assembly. The Senate and the House pass laws for the state. A state's supreme court is the highest court in its judicial branch.

States cannot create money. This job lies in the domain of the national government. Military branches like the U.S. Army and Navy are run by the national government. A state's military is called the National Guard.

The states are in charge of schools and parks. They have traffic laws and police. Can you think of other things states do?

Genre

Expository Text tells people something. It contains facts about real people, things, or events.

Text Feature

A **bar graph** is a chart with parallel bars. The bars represent different quantities.

Think Link

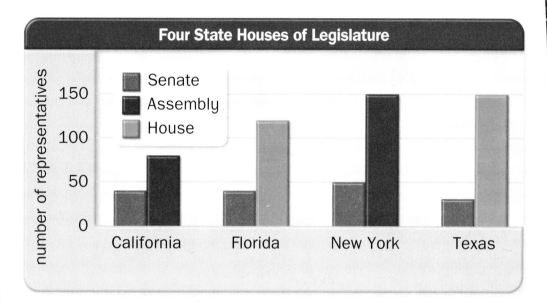

Four State Houses of Legislature

number of representatives

- Senate
- Assembly
- House

150

100

50

0

California   Florida   New York   Texas

1. Look at the bar graph. Why do you think each state has fewer people in the Senate than in the House (or Assembly)?

2. How are the California and federal governments alike? How are they different?

3. What do you think would happen if California could make its own money?

WebLink

Visit **www.ImagineItReading.com/ AtHome** for more information about California's government system.

Apply

Bar Graphs As you work on your investigation, think about how you can use a bar graph to show your facts.

CALIFORNIA

READING: VOCABULARY AND CONCEPT DEVELOPMENT 1.3 Use knowledge of root words to determine the meaning of unknown words within a passage.

Read the story to find the meanings of these words, which are also in "Striking It Rich":

✦ roamed
✦ deserted
✦ canteens
✦ elegant
✦ abundance
✦ impressed
✦ typical
✦ distract
✦ rumors
✦ trapper
✦ territory
✦ hardships

Vocabulary Development

Context Clues are hints in the text that help you find the meanings of words. Look at the words *distract* and *rumors*. Use context clues to find each word's meaning.

Vocabulary

Warm-Up

Elizabeth and her family had just moved into their new home. This was the second time Elizabeth had moved. The first thing she liked to do was check out her new street and see what it was like. As soon as her protective gear was unpacked, she roamed the deserted street on her bicycle.

While Elizabeth rode on the sidewalk, she noticed a cute dog in front of a house. She stopped near the dog to drink from one of the canteens that she had filled with water.

The dog wore an elegant collar. "Wow, your owners must have an abundance of money!" she told the dog.

Having heard that most dogs follow people around, Elizabeth was impressed to discover that this pet was not a typical dog. The dog stayed close to its yard even when she tried to distract it. The owners had trained their dog well.

As she rode away, an animal control van slowly drove past her. Perhaps the rumors she heard were true. The dog trapper for this territory of the city was out picking up dogs without collars. This was a good reason to train a dog to stay in its yard!

Elizabeth wished she could have a dog like this one. However, with the hardships of moving and her brother being allergic to dogs, she would have to settle for visiting this dog.

Elizabeth pedaled home as fast as she could to tell her parents about the cute, obedient dog she had met on her first bike ride. This was going to be a great neighborhood to live in.

Vocabulary Word Web

On a sheet of paper, write a word in the center of the semantic map. Put examples of that word in the top half of your map. Put words that are not examples in the bottom half of the map. Discuss your results with a partner.

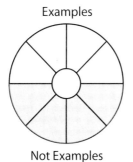

Examples

Not Examples

Concept Vocabulary

This lesson's concept word is **gold rush.** In a *gold rush,* people race to locations where gold has been discovered in an attempt to get rich. Why do you think money is so important to some people, and not others? Why would people rather discover gold than earn their money the old-fashioned way by working hard? What other ways do people become rich quickly?

CALIFORNIA

READING:
COMPREHENSION AND
ANALYSIS OF GRADE-
LEVEL-APPROPRIATE TEXT

2.2 Use appropriate strategies when
reading for different purposes (e.g., full
comprehension, location of information,
personal enjoyment).

Genre

Expository Text
tells people something.
It contains facts about real
people, things, or events.

Comprehension
Strategy

☆ **Asking Questions**
As you read, ask
questions about
things or events in the
text. Look for the answers
as you continue to read
the selection.

STRIKING

The Story
of the
California Gold Rush

by Stephen Krensky

IT RICH

How did the Gold Rush change the United States? What makes people leave their homes to chase a dream?

GOLD

Sutter's Mill

The news was big if it was true—but was it? San Francisco might be a sleepy little town, but it had heard these stories before. There were always plenty of rumors, boasts, and outright lies when it came to finding gold in the hills.

The facts behind this latest story were plain enough. They began with James Marshall, a carpenter. He was helping to build a sawmill on the American River, a hundred miles to the east.

Marshall had little education, but he had sharp eyes and was nobody's fool. On January 24, 1848, he was digging in the riverbed. There he spotted a glittering yellow rock, no bigger than his thumbnail.

Gold, thought Marshall, or maybe iron pyrite, which looks like gold but is more brittle. He struck the metal with a hammer. It flattened but did not break—a good sign. But Marshall was a busy man. He stuck the rock in his hat and went back to work.

Gold

Iron Pyrite
(Fool's Gold)

Later, he rode to Sutter's Fort to see his boss, John A. Sutter. Born in Switzerland, Sutter had been a farmer, a trader, and a fur trapper. He had never been too successful.

Sutter and Marshall carefully examined the rock. They bit it to see if it was soft like gold. It was. They dabbed it with acid to see if its shine would dim. It didn't. Then they weighed it against silver and other things they knew were lighter than gold.

The rock passed every test. It was gold, all right.

Sutter told Marshall to keep the gold a secret. It might not amount to much, but it could still distract the men from their jobs.

But secrets like that don't last. Sutter's men soon learned what Marshall had found. On Sundays, their day off, they began to look for nuggets and gold dust. Some workers collected enough gold in an hour to equal a month's pay.

Sutter's Fort

249

By the spring of 1848, more and more tales were reaching San Francisco, which was home to 800 people. Miners were bragging about scraping gold off rocks with their knives. Why, one fellow had hit a $50 nugget while digging a hole for his tent pole.

Didn't there have to be a little truth to these reports? Many people thought so, and the gold fever spread. Lawyers dropped their clients and soldiers deserted their posts. The schoolhouse closed after its only teacher ran off. Then the mayor disappeared. And nobody could complain to the sheriff because he was gone, too.

By the end of June, San Francisco was almost a ghost town. Stores were empty. Doors blew open in the wind. Dogs roamed the streets and wooden sidewalks with only their shadows for company.

Everyone, it seemed, had left for the hills.

Heading West

During the summer of 1848, the news spread slowly eastward. It rode across the prairie on horseback. It paddled up the Mississippi River on steamboats. It blew around South America on sailing ships.

At first, people back East were not much impressed. Nobody was sure if the stories were true. After all, talk was cheap, and California was far away.

Most Americans didn't know much about California. The territory had only been part of the United States for a few months, since the end of the Mexican War. Its population was small and scattered—a mixture of native tribes, Mexican settlers, and a few American pioneers.

Before long, though, California was on everyone's mind. By November, the New York City newspapers were filled with stories about gold. There was talk of streets paved with gold and nuggets as big as apples lying on the ground.

Then in December, President James K. Polk spoke to Congress about the gold strike. Based on reports from the army and government officials, his speech mentioned "extensive" mines. "The abundance of gold. . ." he said, "would scarcely command belief. . . ."

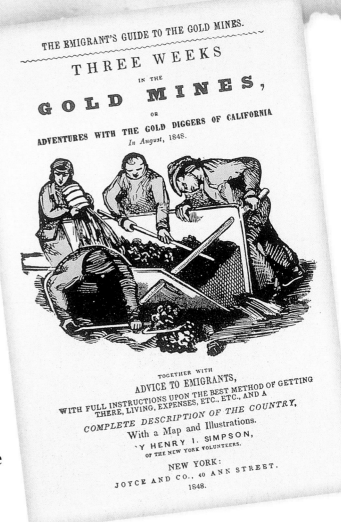

That settled it. Even those people who didn't believe the newspapers had faith in the president. He was bound to know the truth.

Now California was the place to go. In 1848, a decent job as a store clerk or farmhand might be worth $7 a week. A miner could collect four times that much between breakfast and lunch.

It all sounded so simple. Spend a few months in California and then return home, pockets filled with gold. The thousands of dreamers who believed this were almost all men and were mostly young, though one was a ninety-year-old Revolutionary War veteran. Few traveled with their wives or children—if they had them—because they didn't plan to stay very long.

First, though, the miners had to get to California. One hopeful inventor offered a trip by flying machine. But his balloon-floating ship never got off the ground. Instead, travelers went by land or sea.

The sea route, the favorite of Easterners, went down around South America and back up to San Francisco. Hundreds of ships, from elegant clippers to leaky barges, made the trip. The 15,000-mile voyage took from six months to a year.

Most ships were cramped and crowded. One put so many people into a single room that they had to sleep standing up. Sometimes the passengers were from the same town and knew each other. Often everyone was a stranger, wary of other travelers.

On such a long voyage, many passengers got seasick and could not eat. The rest weren't much luckier. The meals had odd names, like *lobscouse* and *hushamagrundy*. The ingredients—including salted meat and moldy bread—were even odder. One passenger wrote that his favorite food was anything with dark molasses, because it hid the mold and killed the bugs.

By the end, most sea travelers were tired, sick, hungry, bored silly, and in need of a bath. Some had gambled away their savings. Many were in poor health. But almost all the hurts or hardships were forgotten at the first sight of San Francisco Bay.

People from the Midwest favored the land route to California. From Missouri the trip was 1,800 miles by wagon train—although one man walked the distance with his belongings in a wheelbarrow. A typical wagon was ten feet long, four feet wide, and pulled by oxen or mules. The wagon train might have just a few wagons or several dozen.

The wagon master led the train and settled any problems along the way. He also gave out chores—gathering firewood or water, keeping lookout, or cooking food. One wagon train even made its members change their underwear each week and carry three pounds of soap for baths.

Days on the trail were long, dusty, and hot. The ride was bumpy. Travelers carried weapons to defend themselves from rattlesnakes, grizzly bears, and Indians. But more men were killed by accidents with guns than by any run-ins they had along the trail.

One big killer on the trail was cholera, a disease caused by a bacteria found in water. It passed through rivers, wells, even canteens—and it acted fast. A man could feel feverish in the morning and be dead by sunset. Cholera claimed thousands of lives among the gold-seekers during the spring and summer of 1849.

The third route to California took the least time if things went well, but they rarely did go well. Travelers took a boat ride to Central America, walked sixty miles across Panama, and took another boat ride up to California.

The sea trips held few dangers because they were brief. The overland walk was the tricky part. The Panama jungle was hot and filled with mosquitoes that carried malaria, a usually fatal disease.

The jungle also was home to flamingoes, parrots, and monkeys. But most travelers were in too much of a hurry to notice.

Whether they came by boat or wagon train, about 80,000 people reached California in 1849. These were the Forty-Niners, hopeful miners who had survived the worst trip of their lives. They could afford to smile and shake one another's hands. Now, they thought, their worries were over.

Stephen Krensky

Stephen Krensky did not have the kind of childhood anyone would choose to write books about. It was happy and uneventful, with only the occasional bump in the night to keep him on his toes. He started writing in college and his first book was published in 1977, two years after he graduated. He is now the author of more than 100 fiction and nonfiction children's books, including novels, picture books, easy readers, and biographies. When Krensky feels he has spent enough time hunched over his computer, he likes to play tennis and softball. He and his family live in Lexington, Massachusetts.

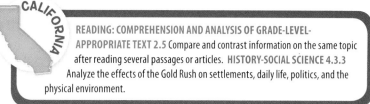

READING: COMPREHENSION AND ANALYSIS OF GRADE-LEVEL-APPROPRIATE TEXT 2.5 Compare and contrast information on the same topic after reading several passages or articles. HISTORY-SOCIAL SCIENCE 4.3.3 Analyze the effects of the Gold Rush on settlements, daily life, politics, and the physical environment.

Theme Connections

Discuss

Within the Selection

1. How do Sutter and Marshall know that the rock they found is gold?

2. What three routes could people take to get to California?

Across Selections

3. James Marshall finds gold in a river. Which selection explains how water gets into rivers or streams?

4. How has California changed since "The First Californians"? What changes do you see in our economy or our environment?

Beyond the Selection

5. Which route would you have taken to California?

6. If you struck gold and became rich, what would you do with all your money?

Write

Describe a time you found something valuable.

Read

Look for books and magazine articles about the California Gold Rush to read on your own.

CALIFORNIA

SCIENCE: EARTH SCIENCES
4.a Students know how to differentiate among igneous, sedimentary, and metamorphic rocks by referring to their properties and methods of formation (the rock cycle).

Science Link

THE ROCK CYCLE

Genre

Expository Text tells people something. It contains facts about real people, things, or events.

Text Feature

A **pie chart** is a circle-shaped graph that represents an amount. It is divided into sections that look like pie slices. Each "slice" shows a percentage of the total amount.

Each rock you find today has been created in the rock cycle. Rocks, which are made of minerals found within Earth, form in three ways.

Igneous rocks form when magma cools and hardens. Magma is a hot liquid inside Earth that is made of minerals. When magma reaches Earth's surface, it is called lava. The lava forms crystals as it cools and creates igneous rock.

Sedimentary rocks are formed in layers. Wind and water break rocks into pieces. Then the rock pieces are cemented together by pressure with bits of bones and shells. They harden in layers.

A metamorphic rock is a result of high temperature and pressure, which change the chemical form of the rock. Metamorphic rocks are the hardest rocks. Marble is one example.

Any rock can become a metamorphic with enough heat and pressure. All rocks can erode and break into pieces, so any rock can become sedimentary. Each kind of rock can also melt into magma and then cool into an igneous rock.

So, the next time you pick up a typical rock, imagine it becoming a completely different type of rock in the rock cycle.

Think Link

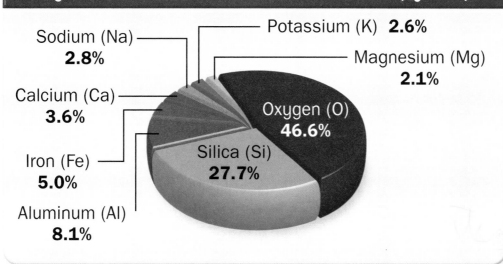

Eight most common elements in the Earth's crust (by mass)

Sodium (Na)
2.8%

Potassium (K) **2.6%**

Calcium (Ca)
3.6%

Magnesium (Mg)
2.1%

Iron (Fe)
5.0%

Oxygen (O)
46.6%

Silica (Si)
27.7%

Aluminum (Al)
8.1%

1. Look at the pie chart. Which element is the most abundant in Earth's crust?

2. How are sedimentary rocks formed?

3. How might volcanoes and igneous rock be related?

CALIFORNIA WebLink

Visit **www.ImagineItReading.com/ AtHome** for more information about the rock cycle.

Apply

Pie Charts As you work on your investigation, think about how pie charts can help you explain your ideas.

CALIFORNIA

READING: VOCABULARY AND CONCEPT DEVELOPMENT 1.2 Apply knowledge of word origins, derivations, synonyms, antonyms, and idioms to determine the meaning of words and phrases. 1.3 Use knowledge of root words to determine the meaning of unknown words within a passage.

A Covered Wagon Girl
The Diary of Sallie Hester, 1849–1850

edited by Christy Steele with Ann Hodgson

Genre

Comprehension Strategy

Read the story to find the meanings of these words, which are also in "A Covered Wagon Girl":

◆ climate
◆ advance
◆ vast
◆ dilapidated
◆ tremendous
◆ scarce
◆ provisions
◆ engaged
◆ perilous
◆ detained
◆ emigrants
◆ omen

Vocabulary Development

Context Clues are hints in the text that help you find the meanings of words. What do *engaged* and *provisions* mean?

Vocabulary

Warm-Up

Chad and his family had been planning a vacation to the beach for months. They loved the climate of the area. But two days before the trip, a hurricane hit with little advance warning. The damage was vast. The condo Chad's family had rented was destroyed.

Chad's father asked the family where they wanted to vacation instead. Chad and his brother, Kevin, had the same idea.

"Let's help the hurricane victims," Chad suggested.

The next evening, Chad's dad said, "I found a place where we can help. There is a dilapidated section of the city where the storm hit the hardest. There is a tremendous need for volunteers. Help is scarce."

Two days later they loaded up their minivan with provisions.

"Enjoy these last few hours of relaxation," Chad's mom said. "When we get there, we will be engaged in hard work all day, every day. Things could be perilous there."

They finally reached their destination. Chad's father pulled a piece of paper from his wallet.

"What is that, Dad?" asked Kevin.

"My friend Bob gave me the name and address of a person to contact here. He said that I should show this paper if we were detained by security. They would show us where to go."

They found the temporary shelter with no problems. At the shelter they met a family of emigrants who had lost everything. Chad and Kevin immediately began unloading bottled water, food, and blankets from the van.

"Thank you so much for coming," said an older man wearing a red vest with the word "Volunteer" across the front. Everyone at the shelter felt our arrival was an omen of better days to come.

"We are just glad we can help," said Chad.

Vocabulary Word Play

On a separate sheet of paper, write original sentences using six of the vocabulary words. Then think of a synonym for each vocabulary word, and rewrite the sentences using the synonyms correctly. Read your sentences to your partner.

Concept Vocabulary

This lesson's concept word is *migration. Migration* is the movement of people or animals from one place to another. If you had to migrate to another place, where would you go? Who would you take with you? How would you get there? What would the trip be like? On a piece of paper, write a short paragraph about your imaginary migration, and share it with a classmate.

CALIFORNIA

READING:
COMPREHENSION AND
ANALYSIS OF GRADE-
LEVEL-APPROPRIATE TEXT

2.2 Use appropriate strategies when
reading for different purposes (e.g., full
comprehension, location of information,
personal enjoyment).

Genre

A **diary** is a first-person
account of memorable
events in someone's life.
Entries are made regularly,
and the date is usually
noted.

Comprehension Strategy

Visualizing
As you read, form
mental images of
the setting, characters, and
actions to help you better
understand the selection.

A Covered Wagon Girl

The Diary of Sallie Hester, 1849–1850

edited by Christy Steele with Ann Hodgson

Focus Questions

What would the United States be like if there had been no pioneers? What is it like to travel across the country in a wagon?

Bloomington, Indiana, March 20, 1849 —

Our family, consisting of father, mother, two brothers, and one sister, left this morning for that far and much talked of country, California. My father started our wagons one month in advance, to St. Joseph, Missouri, our starting point. We take the steamboat at New Albany [Indiana], going by water to St. Joe. The train leaving Bloomington on that memorable occasion was called the Missionary Train, from the fact that the Rev. Isaac Owens of the Methodist Church and a number of ministers of the same denomination were sent as missionaries to California. Our train numbered fifty wagons. The last hours were spent in bidding good bye to old friends. My mother is heartbroken over this separation of relatives and friends. Giving up old associations for what? Good health, perhaps. My father is going in search of health, not gold. The last good bye has been said—the last glimpse of our old home on the hill, and a wave of hand at the old Academy with a good bye to kind teachers and schoolmates, and we are off. We have been several days reaching New Albany on account of the terrible conditions of the roads. Our carriage upset at one place. All were thrown out, but no one was hurt. We were detained several hours on account of this accident. My mother thought it a bad omen and wanted to return and give up the trip.

New Albany, March 24 —

This is my first experience of a big city and my first glimpse of a river and steamboats.

March 26 —

Took the steamboat Meteor this evening for St. Joe. Now sailing on the broad Ohio, toward the far West.

April 3 —

On the Missouri River, the worst in the world, sticking on sand bars most of the time.

April 14 —

Our boat struck another sand bar and was obliged to land passengers ten miles below St. Joe. Having our carriage with us, we were more fortunate than others…

St. Joe, [Missouri,] April 27 —

Here we are at last, safe and sound. We expect to remain here several days, laying in supplies for the trip and waiting our turn to be ferried across the river. As far as the eye can reach, so great is the emigration, you see nothing but wagons. This town presents a striking appearance—a vast army on wheels—crowds of men, women, and lots of children and last but not least the cattle and horses upon which our lives depend.

May 21 —

Camped on the beautiful Blue River, 215 miles from St. Joe, with plenty of wood and water and good grazing for our cattle. Our family all in good health. When we left St. Joe my mother had to be lifted in and out of our wagons; now she walks a mile or two without stopping, and gets in and out of the wagons as spry as a young girl. She is perfectly well. We had two deaths in our train within the past week of cholera— young men going West to seek their fortunes. We buried them on the banks of the Blue River, far from home and friends. This is a beautiful spot. The Plains are covered with flowers. . . . When we camp at night, we form a corral with our wagons and pitch our tents on the outside, and inside of this corral we drive our cattle, with guards stationed on the outside of tents. We have a cooking stove made of sheet iron, a portable table, tin plates and cups, cheap knives and forks (best ones packed away), camp stools, etc. We sleep in our wagons on feather beds; the men who drive for us [sleep] in the tent. We live on bacon, ham, rice, dried fruits, molasses, packed butter, bread, coffee, tea, and milk as we have our own cows. Occasionally some of the men kill an antelope and then we have a feast; and sometimes we have fish on Sunday.

June 3 —

Our tent is now pitched on the beautiful Platte River, 315 miles from St. Joe. The cholera is raging. A great many deaths; graves everywhere. We as a company are all in good health. Game is scarce; a few antelope in sight. Roads bad.

Goose Creek, June 17 —

This is our day of rest. There are several encampments in sight, making one feel not quite out of civilization . . . Passed this week Court House Rock. Twelve miles from this point is Chimney Rock, 230 feet in height.

Chimney Rock

Fort Laramie, [Wyoming,] June 19 —

This fort is of adobe, enclosed with a high wall of the same. The entrance is a hole in the wall just large enough for a person to crawl through. The impression you have on entering is that you are in a small town. Men were engaged in all kinds of business from blacksmith up. We stayed here some time looking at everything that was to be seen and enjoying it to the fullest extent after our long tramp. We camped one mile from the fort, where we remained a few days to wash and lighten up.

Fort Laramie

June 21 —

Left camp and started over the Black Hills, sixty miles over the worst road in the world. Have again struck the Platte and followed it until we came to the ferry. Here we had a great deal of trouble swimming our cattle across, taking our wagons to pieces, unloading and replacing our traps. A number of accidents happened here. A lady and four children were drowned through the carelessness of those in charge of the ferry.

July 2 —

Passed Independence Rock. This rock is covered with names. With great difficulty I found a place to cut mine. Twelve miles from this is Devil's Gate. It's an opening in the mountain through which the Sweetwater River flows. Several of us climbed this mountain—somewhat perilous for youngsters not over fourteen. We made our way to the very edge of the cliff and looked down. We could hear the water dashing, splashing and roaring as if angry at the small space through which it was forced to pass. We were gone so long that the train was stopped and men were sent out in search of us. We made all sorts of promises to remain in sight in the future. John Owens, a son of the minister, my brother John, sister Lottie and myself were the quartet. During the week we passed the South Pass and the summit of the Rocky Mountains. Four miles from here are the Pacific Springs.

Independence Rock

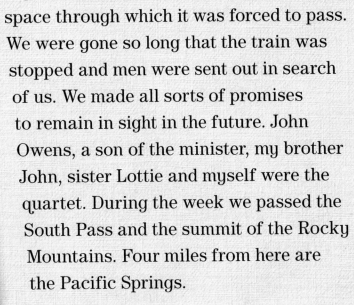

Devil's Gate

Green River

July 4 —

. . . At this point saw lots of dead cattle left by the emigrants to starve and die. Took a cutoff; had neither wood nor water for fifty-two miles. Traveled in the night. Arrived at Green River next day at two o'clock in the afternoon. Lay by two days to rest man and beast after our long and weary journey.

July 29 —

Passed Soda Springs [Idaho]. Two miles further on are the Steamboat Springs. They puff and blow and throw the water high in the air. The springs are in the midst of a grove of trees, a beautiful and romantic spot.

August 3 —

Took another cut-off this week called Sublets [Sublette's Cutoff]. Struck Raft River; from thence to Swamp Creek. Passed some beautiful scenery, high cliffs of rocks resembling old ruins or dilapidated buildings.

Hot Springs, August 18 —

Camped on a branch of St. Mary's River, a very disagreeable and unpleasant place on account of the water being so hot. This week some of our company left us, all young men. They were jolly, merry fellows and gave life to our lonely evenings. We all miss them very much. Some had violins, others guitars, and some had fine voices, and they always had a good audience. They were anxious to hurry on without the Sunday stops. Roads are rocky and trying to our wagons, and the dust is horrible. The men wear veils tied over their hats as a protection. When we reach camp at night they are covered with dust from head to heels.

Humboldt River [Nevada,] August 20 —

We are now 348 miles from the mines. We expect to travel that distance in three weeks and a half. Water and grass scarce.

St. Mary's River, August 25 —

Still traveling down the Humboldt. Grass has been scarce until today. Though the water is not fit to drink—slough water— we are obliged to use it, for it's all we have.

September 4 —

Left the place [St. Mary's] where we camped last Sunday. Traveled six miles. Stopped and cut grass for the cattle and supplied ourselves with water for the desert. Had a trying time crossing. Several of our cattle gave out and we left one. Our journey through the desert was from Monday, three o'clock in the afternoon, until Thursday morning at sunrise, September 6. The weary journey last night, the mooing of the cattle for water, their exhausted condition, with the cry of "Another ox down," the stopping of train to unyoke the poor dying brute, to let him follow at will or stop by the wayside and die, and the weary, weary tramp of men and beasts worn out with heat and famished for water, will never be erased from my memory. Just at dawn, in the distance, we had a glimpse of the Truckee River, and with it the feeling: Saved at last! Poor cattle; they kept on mooing, even when they stood knee deep in water. The long dreaded desert had been crossed and we are all safe and well. Here we rested Thursday and Friday—grass green and beautiful, and the cattle are up to their eyes in it.

September 8 —

Traveled fourteen miles; crossed Truckee twelve times.

September 11 —

Made eighteen miles. Crossed Truckee River ten times. Came near being drowned at one of the crossings. Got frightened and jumped out of the carriage into the water. The current was very swift and carried me some distance down the stream.

Truckee River

September 14 —

. . . We crossed the summit of the Sierra Nevada. It was night when we reached the top, and I shall never forget our descent to the place where we are now encamped—our tedious march with pine knots blazing in the darkness and the tall, majestic pines towering above our heads. The scene was grand and gloomy beyond description. We could not ride—roads too narrow and rocky—so we trudged along, keeping pace with the wagons as best we could. This is another picture engraven upon the tablets of memory. It was a footsore and weary crowd that reached that night our present camping place.

Yuba Valley [California,] September 16 —

We are now 108 miles from Sutter's Fort.

September 19 —

Started once more. Roads bad, almost impassable. After traveling for twenty-five miles we halted for one day. Good grass three miles from camp.

September 21 —

Reached Bear Valley by descending a tremendous hill. We let the wagons down with ropes. Stopped over Sunday. At Sleepy Hollow we again let our wagons down the mountain with ropes. Rested in the hollow, ate our dinner and then commenced our weary march over the mountain. Left one of our wagons and the springs of our carriage. Cut down trees for our cattle to browse on. Thanks to a kind Providence we are nearing the end of our long and perilous journey. Came on to Grass Valley and rested four or five days.

Vernon, California [near San Francisco,] October 6 —

Well, after a five month's trip from St. Joe, Missouri, our party of fifty wagons, now only thirteen, has at last reached this haven of rest. Strangers in a strange land—what will our future be? . . .

Fremont, [California,] October 10 —

This is a small town on the opposite side of the river from Vernon. My father had decided to remain here for the winter, as the rains have set in and we are worn out. We have had a small house put up of two rooms made of boards with puncheon floor. On this mother has a carpet which she brought with us and we feel quite fine, as our neighbors have the ground for a floor. The rooms are lined with heavy blue cloth. Our beds are put up in bunk style on one side of the room and curtained off. Back of these rooms we have pitched our tent, which answers as a store room, and the back of the lot is enclosed with a brush fence. My father has gone to Sacramento to lay in provisions for the winter.

Fremont, December 20 —

Have not written or confided in thee, dear journal, for some time. Now I must write up. My father returned from Sacramento with a supply of provisions. Everything is enormously high. Carpenter's wages sixteen dollars per day; vegetables scarce and high; potatoes the principal vegetable; onions, fifty cents each; eggs, one dollar apiece; melons, five dollars, and apples, one dollar each. The rain is pouring down. River very high.

January 12 [1850] —

Water over the banks of the river, all over town except in a few places. Our house has escaped, though it's all around us. Mother has planted a garden in the rear of [the] lot and that has been swept away. Nearly everybody is up to their knees in mud and water. Some have boots. As far as the eye can reach you see nothing but water. It's horrible. Wish I was back in Indiana. Snakes are plenty. They come down the river, crawl under our bed and everywhere.

January 20 —

Water receding.

Fremont, February 27 —

It's raining very hard. A little snow by way of variety. Horrible weather. Received several letters from schoolmates at home.

April 1 —

Quite a number of our old friends who crossed the Plains with us have stopped here for the winter, which makes it pleasant for mother. My father has gone to San Jose . . . to look for a permanent home.

April 27 —

My father has returned from San Jose. He gives glowing accounts of the place and lovely climate. We have not seen very much as yet of the mild and delightful climate of California so much talked about. We leave next month for San Jose. We are all glad that we are going to have a home somewhere at last.

Meet the Author

Sallie Hester

Hester never knew her diary would become a book. When she wrote it, her story was not unique. Her family was one of thousands going west on the Oregon Trail. Lots of other families were in her wagon train. They all wanted a better life in California. The trip took more than a year. Her diary helps us see that pioneers were real people. It brings history to life.

Meet the Editors

Christy Steele

Steele has helped create many children's books. Some of her books tell about people who lived long ago. Others tell about different kinds of animals and interesting places. Steele lives in Milwaukee, Wisconsin.

Ann Hodgson

Hodgson helped write two books about girls who lived long ago. She also helped make lists that show who was married in parts of Illinois more than one hundred years ago. Hodgson lives in Minneapolis, Minnesota.

Theme Connections

Discuss

Within the Selection

1. Why does Sallie's father take his family west?

2. Where does Sallie Hester carve her name?

Across Selections

3. How are "A Covered Wagon Girl: The Diary of Sallie Hester, 1840–1850" and "Striking It Rich: The Story of the California Gold Rush" similar?

4. Compare and contrast Sallie Hester and Karana from "Island of the Blue Dolphins."

Beyond the Selection

5. The December 20 diary entry shows that food prices were very high. Why might this have happened?

6. What is the longest trip you have ever taken? What were the best and worst parts of it?

Write

Describe your day as though you were writing in a diary.

Read

Look for books and diaries from other pioneers who headed west to California to establish new lives.

CALIFORNIA

HISTORY-SOCIAL
SCIENCE 4.2.3 Describe
the Spanish exploration
and colonization of California,
including the relationships among
soldiers, missionaries, and Indians (e.g.,
Juan Crespi, Junipero Serra, Gaspar de
Portola). 4.2.4 Describe the mapping of,
geographic basis of, and economic factors
in the placement and function of the
Spanish missions; and understand how the
mission system expanded the influence
of Spain and Catholicism throughout New
Spain and Latin America. 4.2.5 Describe
the daily lives of the people, native and
nonnative, who occupied the presidios,
missions, ranchos, and pueblos. 4.2.7
Describe the effects of the Mexican War
for Independence on Alta California,
including its effects on the territorial
boundaries of North America.

Social Studies Link

Spanish Missions

In the 1600s, people from Spain came to California and Texas. Native Americans had lived in this vast territory for many years in peace.

Catholic missionaries arrived from Spain too. They wanted Native Americans to become Christians like they were. The Native Americans did not want to change.

The first California mission opened in 1769. By 1823, there were more than twenty of them. Many were started in Texas too.

The missionaries taught the Native Americans about their religion and how to farm. They taught them how to build sturdy buildings. Many Native Americans were happy at first, but that changed. They were forced to work like slaves.

Some of them tried to run away, and some tried to fight. Many were killed. It was a perilous time. Others died from diseases that the Spanish brought with them from Spain. The Native Americans were not used to these diseases.

In 1821, Mexico won its independence from Spain. The missions began to close. Many missions were sold to be used as ranches.

Genre

Expository Text tells people something. It contains facts about real people, things, or events.

Text Feature

Captions explain what is happening in a photograph.

Mission San José in Texas

Mission San Antonio de Padua in California

1. Read the captions that go with the photographs. If you had to rewrite the captions, what would they say?

2. How did the missions change California starting in 1769?

3. What was the purpose of the mission system?

CALIFORNIA WebLink

Visit **www.ImagineItReading.com/ AtHome** for more information about the Spanish mission system in California.

Apply

Captions As you work on your investigation, think about how captions might help you highlight facts.

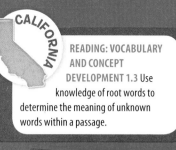

READING: VOCABULARY AND CONCEPT DEVELOPMENT 1.3 Use knowledge of root words to determine the meaning of unknown words within a passage.

Read the story to find the meanings of these words, which are also in "The Earth Dragon Awakes":

✦ eerie
✦ prominent
✦ cisterns
✦ scrabble
✦ aftershock
✦ billowing
✦ timbers
✦ debris
✦ rubble
✦ stampede
✦ daggers
✦ hoarse

Vocabulary Development

Context Clues are hints in the text that help you find the meanings of words. Use context clues to find the meanings of *cisterns* and *scrabble*.

Vocabulary

Warm-Up

I stared into the valley and up at the volcano with an eerie feeling building in my chest. "Are we really going to hike on Mount St. Helens?" I asked my dad.

"We sure are! It'll be fun! We have a prominent geologist leading us, so we will be safe," my dad replied.

My sister and I walked over to the large cisterns to fill our water bottles for the daylong hike. I watched a boy scrabble through his backpack looking for his water bottle. It was going to be a hot day.

Dr. Krissek, the geologist leading our hike, told us interesting facts as we walked. He explained that the eruption of the volcano in 1980 was triggered by an earthquake and a strong aftershock. Smoke was billowing from the side of the mountain for nine hours after it erupted.

Just off the path, trees were lying flat on the ground. Dr. Krissek explained that these trees could have been made into timbers, but now they were a part of the debris and rubble from the eruption. Dr. Krissek also mentioned how the animals created a stampede trying to flee the eruption.

At the end of the hike, Dr. Krissek used one of the daggers from his belt to dig into the ground. His voice had become hoarse, so we listened closely as he showed how the forest was already growing back.

I do not know what I was so worried about. I had a great day!

Vocabulary Word Web

Work with a partner. On a sheet of paper, write one of the words in the diamond, and think of other words that explain its meaning. Write these words in the boxes. When you have finished, compare webs with your partner and discuss why you chose certain words.

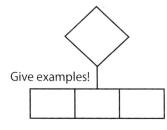

Give examples!

Concept Vocabulary

This lesson's concept word is *earthquake*. An *earthquake* is a shaking of Earth's surface caused by shifting plates in Earth's crust. An earthquake can cause large amounts of damage if it occurs in a highly populated area such as Los Angeles. The best way to prepare for an earthquake is to have an emergency plan for your family. What is the plan your family has if an earthquake strikes? What else could you do to prepare?

CALIFORNIA

READING:
COMPREHENSION AND
ANALYSIS OF GRADE-
LEVEL-APPROPRIATE TEXT

2.2 Use appropriate strategies when
reading for different purposes (e.g., full
comprehension, location of information,
personal enjoyment).

Genre

Historical Fiction

is a realistic story that
takes place in a specific
time in the past. It may be
based on historical events
and actual persons.

Comprehension
Skill

 **Drawing
Conclusions**

Take small pieces of
information from the
text about a character
or an event, and use
this information to
understand something
new about the
character or event.

The Earth Dragon Awakes

by Laurence Yep

illustrations by Scott Goto

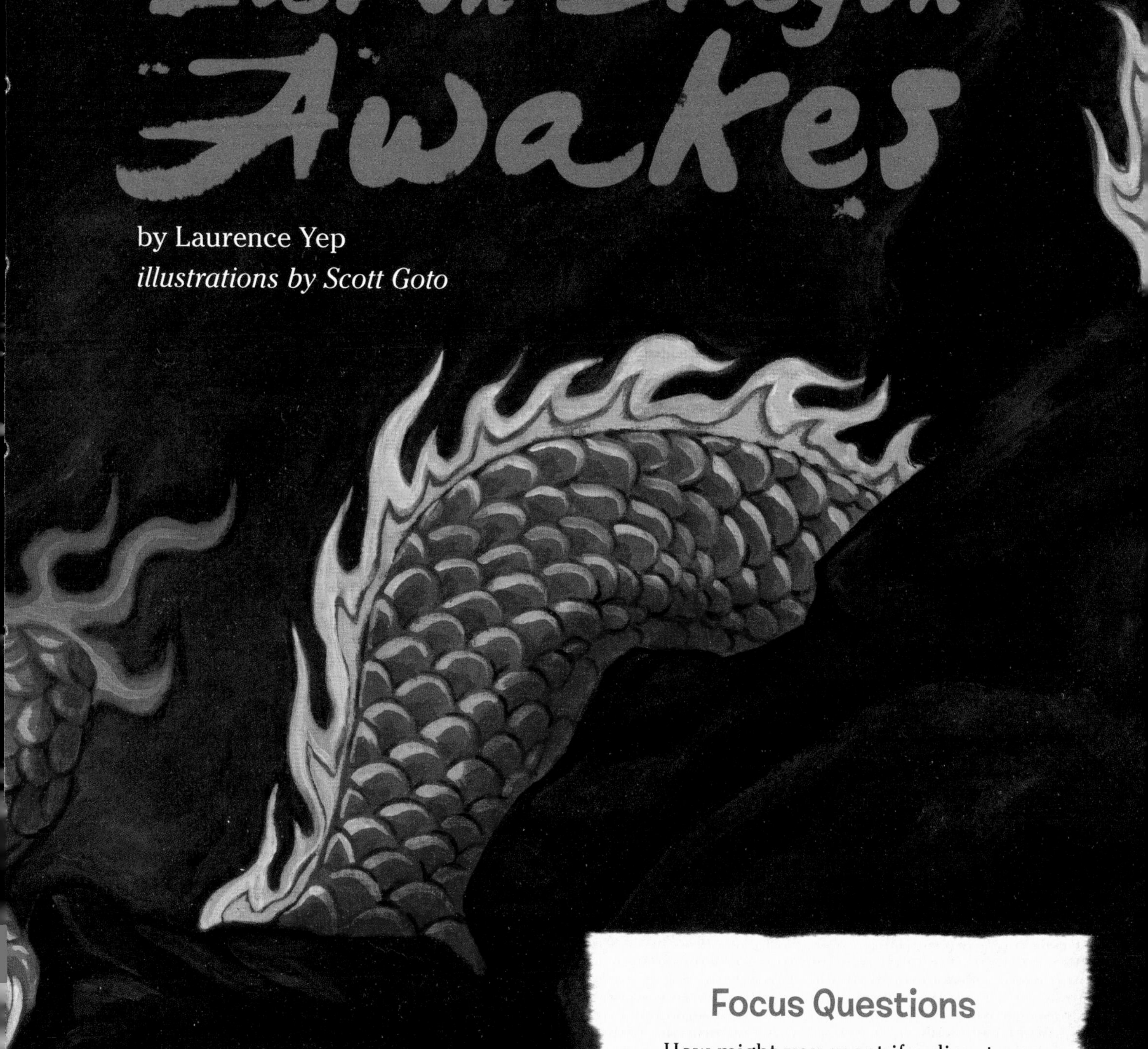

Focus Questions

How might you react if a disaster struck? What would you do for yourself or others to survive?

285

Chin and his father Ah Sing, recent immigrants from China, have made a home in San Francisco, circa 1906. Chin's father works for a prominent banker in the city and Chin has become friends with the banker's son, Henry Travis. And while Chin and Henry come from two completely different worlds, a disaster will bind them—as well as everyone else in the city—together forever.

5:11 A.M.
Wednesday, April 18, 1906
Below San Francisco

Far below San Francisco, the Pacific Plate grinds against the North American Plate. It rubs harder than it ever has. The two plates slip and twist. Dirt and rock stir and tumble. In an instant, 375,000 square miles shake violently.

All over the world, there are machines that measure earthquakes. Their needles start to wag crazily. In those days, scientists measured earthquakes in a different way. Today we use the Richter scale. The Great Earthquake was 8.25 by modern standards.

The surface rips open for almost 290 miles. From Los Angeles in the south to Oregon in the north and east to Nevada, cliffs fall into the ocean, hills crumble into valleys, mountains crack, rivers twist, ancient trees topple and crash.

But San Francisco is at the center of the destruction. It sits on the bull's-eye of a target. In its houses, almost 343,000 people lie sleeping or are just waking.

It is as if more than 18 million sticks of dynamite explode beneath them. That is more force than the atom bomb that struck Hiroshima.

This is the Earthquake of 1906, when the earth shook so terribly.

5:12 A.M.
Wednesday, April 18, 1906
Chin and Ah Sing's tenement
Chinatown

Chin is pouring water from a pitcher into a bowl. He needs to wash up. Then they will catch a cable car to Henry's house to cook breakfast for the Travises.

Suddenly everything trembles. The bowl creeps across the table. Then even the table crawls away. Chin spills water everywhere.

"You can write your mother about your first earthquake," his father says unworriedly.

The floor rolls under them like a wooden sea. The bowl slips over the edge and crashes. Boxes tumble from the stack. Their possessions scatter across the boards. Chin and his father drop to their knees.

Ah Sing tries to sound brave. "The Earth Dragon must be scratching," he laughs.

Chin tries to be just as fearless. When the room stills, he tries to joke like his father. "He must really have an itch."

Before his father can answer, the trembling begins again.

Chin waits for it stop. But it goes on and on. The tenement creaks and groans like an old giant. Their bed and bureau prowl like hungry animals.

Ah Sing crawls over. He puts his arms around Chin. "Don't be scared," he says. Ah Sing's voice sounds funny because he is shaking with the room.

Beneath them, unseen timbers crack like sticks. The next instant, one side of the room tilts upward. They slide helplessly with all the furniture toward the opposite wall. Chin feels like a doll. Their belongings crash and thump as they pile up.

His father forces him under the table.

"The tenement is falling!" his father shouts.

Walls crack and crumble. Windows shatter. Broken glass sprays like little daggers.

Chin's stomach feels funny when the room itself drops. They bounce against the floor as it stops with a jerk. For a moment, they lie there. Their neighbors scream from the middle level. Ah Sing and Chin's room is crushing them.

Then the floor twitches. It plunges again. There are more screams. This time it is the ground level that is smashed.

Their floor gives one final thump and stops.

Dazed, Chin peeks out from beneath the table. He sees cracks. They spread like a crazy spiderweb around all the walls. Spurts of powdery plaster puff out. The walls crumble like paper. The ceiling drops down on them.

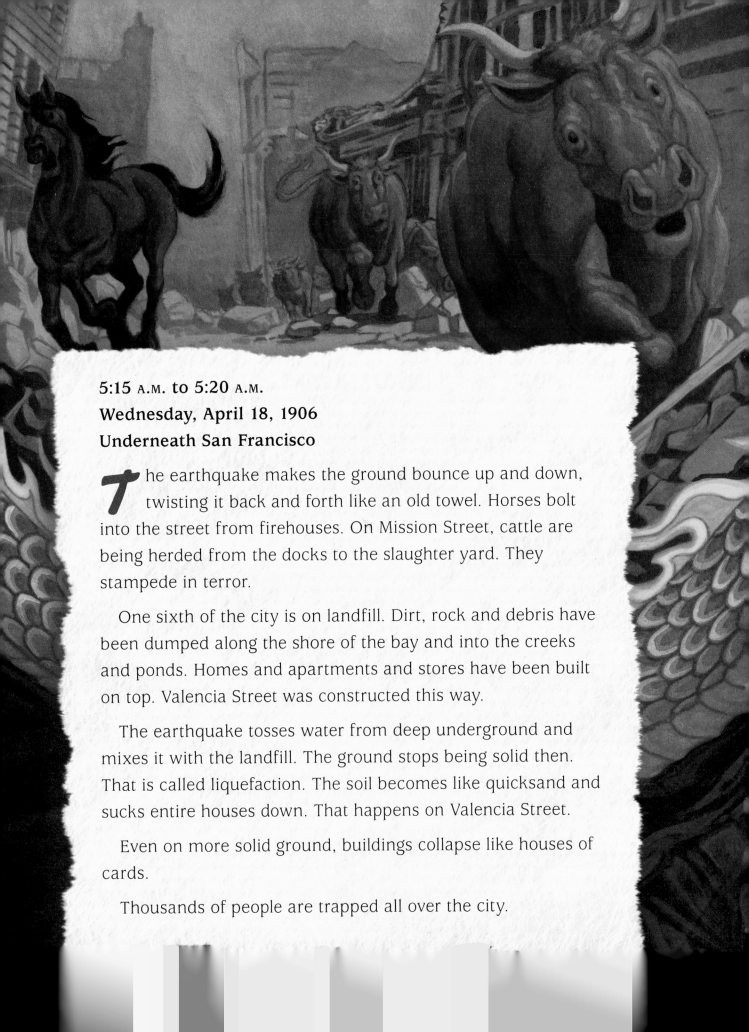

5:15 A.M. to 5:20 A.M.
Wednesday, April 18, 1906
Underneath San Francisco

The earthquake makes the ground bounce up and down, twisting it back and forth like an old towel. Horses bolt into the street from firehouses. On Mission Street, cattle are being herded from the docks to the slaughter yard. They stampede in terror.

One sixth of the city is on landfill. Dirt, rock and debris have been dumped along the shore of the bay and into the creeks and ponds. Homes and apartments and stores have been built on top. Valencia Street was constructed this way.

The earthquake tosses water from deep underground and mixes it with the landfill. The ground stops being solid then. That is called liquefaction. The soil becomes like quicksand and sucks entire houses down. That happens on Valencia Street.

Even on more solid ground, buildings collapse like houses of cards.

Thousands of people are trapped all over the city.

5:20 A.M.
Wednesday, April 18, 1906
Chin and Ah Sing's tenement
Chinatown

Chin cannot see. He cannot move. He can barely breathe.

In the darkness, he hears his father cough. "Are you all right, Chin?"

His father is holding him tight. Chin tries to answer. But dust fills his mouth and throat. So he simply nods. Since his father can't see him, Chin squeezes his arm.

Then he shifts around so he can raise one hand. He can feel the tabletop, but its legs have collapsed. Fallen pieces of ceiling and wall have turned the space into a tiny cave.

His father pushes at the wreckage around him. "It won't budge," he grunts.

Chin shoves with him. "The whole ceiling fell on us." If his father hadn't pulled him under the table, he would have been crushed.

But now they are buried alive.

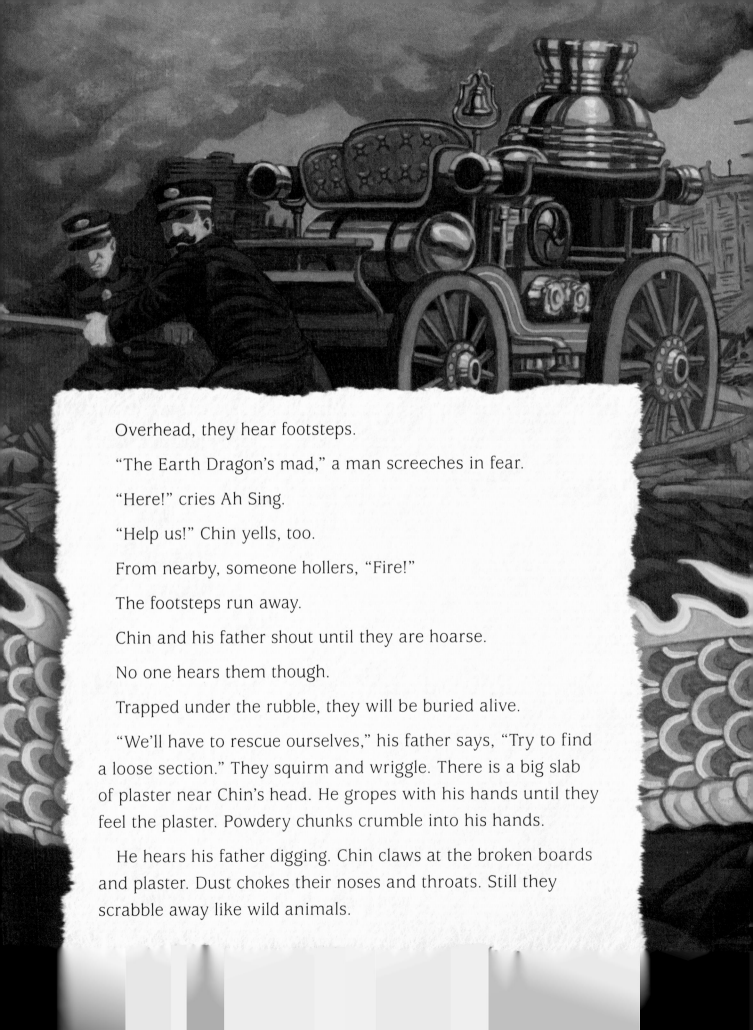

Overhead, they hear footsteps.

"The Earth Dragon's mad," a man screeches in fear.

"Here!" cries Ah Sing.

"Help us!" Chin yells, too.

From nearby, someone hollers, "Fire!"

The footsteps run away.

Chin and his father shout until they are hoarse.

No one hears them though.

Trapped under the rubble, they will be buried alive.

"We'll have to rescue ourselves," his father says, "Try to find a loose section." They squirm and wriggle. There is a big slab of plaster near Chin's head. He gropes with his hands until they feel the plaster. Powdery chunks crumble into his hands.

He hears his father digging. Chin claws at the broken boards and plaster. Dust chokes their noses and throats. Still they scrabble away like wild animals.

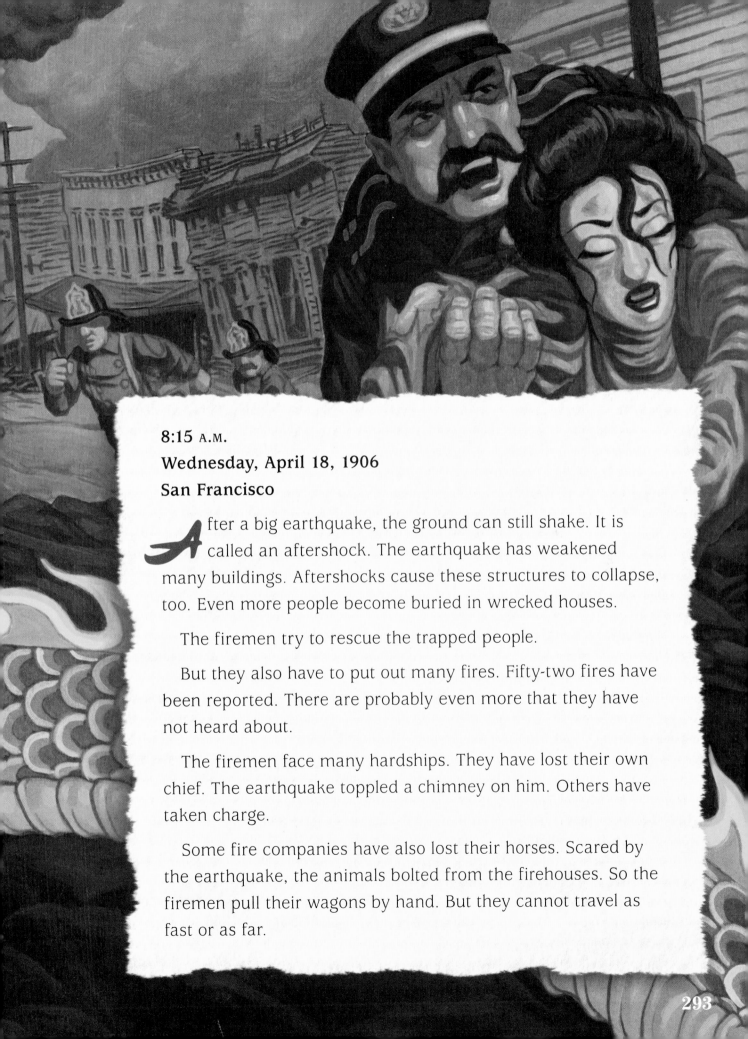

8:15 A.M.
Wednesday, April 18, 1906
San Francisco

After a big earthquake, the ground can still shake. It is called an aftershock. The earthquake has weakened many buildings. Aftershocks cause these structures to collapse, too. Even more people become buried in wrecked houses.

The firemen try to rescue the trapped people.

But they also have to put out many fires. Fifty-two fires have been reported. There are probably even more that they have not heard about.

The firemen face many hardships. They have lost their own chief. The earthquake toppled a chimney on him. Others have taken charge.

Some fire companies have also lost their horses. Scared by the earthquake, the animals bolted from the firehouses. So the firemen pull their wagons by hand. But they cannot travel as fast or as far.

They also don't have enough water. The big water mains have broken in three hundred places. Pipes branch from the water mains into the buildings. There are more than 23,000 breaks in those pipes.

Most hydrants are empty but the firemen do not give up. They find the hydrants that work. They hook up hoses from one wagon to another so they can pump water from several blocks away to a fire. Or they pump salt water from the bay.

But more and more fires flicker into life in the ruins. The flames feed upon broken boards or hissing gas pipes. Soon they swell large enough to swallow entire houses. They are like a pack of wolves attacking where no one expects them to.

Then one fireman remembers an old source of water. Many years ago, water was stored in fifty-seven stone-covered pits called cisterns. Then the city installed water pipes and covered up the old cisterns. Now the firemen break into them.

8:15 A.M. to 10:30 A.M.
Wednesday, April 18, 1906
Chinatown

The Earth Dragon is restless. He tosses and turns on his bed beneath the surface, and more buildings have collapsed in Chinatown. Smoke hangs over Portsmouth Square. Everything looks hazy. Even so, Chin can see new plumes of smoke. Some of them rise from the direction of Henry's house. He thinks again of the firemen without water.

"We should make sure the Travises are okay," Chin says, worried.

With his son's help, Ah Sing gets up from the grass. He tries a few steps. "I can't walk that far. And you can't go there alone."

"They're probably already leaving on a train," Ah Quon says. "And so should we. The fire is spreading. Think of your boy. Isn't he one of the reasons why you came here?"

Chin's father bites his lip. "I just sent my salary back to China. Can you loan us the money?"

Ah Quon pats his empty pockets. "I'm broke, too."

"A hundred dollars! That's piracy," a man shouts from across the street. A merchant in an expensive robe is arguing with a man on a wagon.

The driver spits on the cobblestones. "Then you can watch your stuff burn or be crushed. There's plenty of others willing to pay."

The merchant pulls at his little goatee. "Okay. But you take me and my family, too."

Ah Quon nudges Ah Sing. "I see our train fares." And he yells to the merchant. "Hey, do you need help loading the wagon?"

The merchant stares at Ah Quon's big arms. "You're hired."

Ah Quon pushes Chin forward. "My partner, too."

"He's too small," the merchant snorts.

"He's small but powerful," Ah Quon insists. "I only work with my partner."

The merchant throws up his arms. "The world is full of pirates." But he gives in.

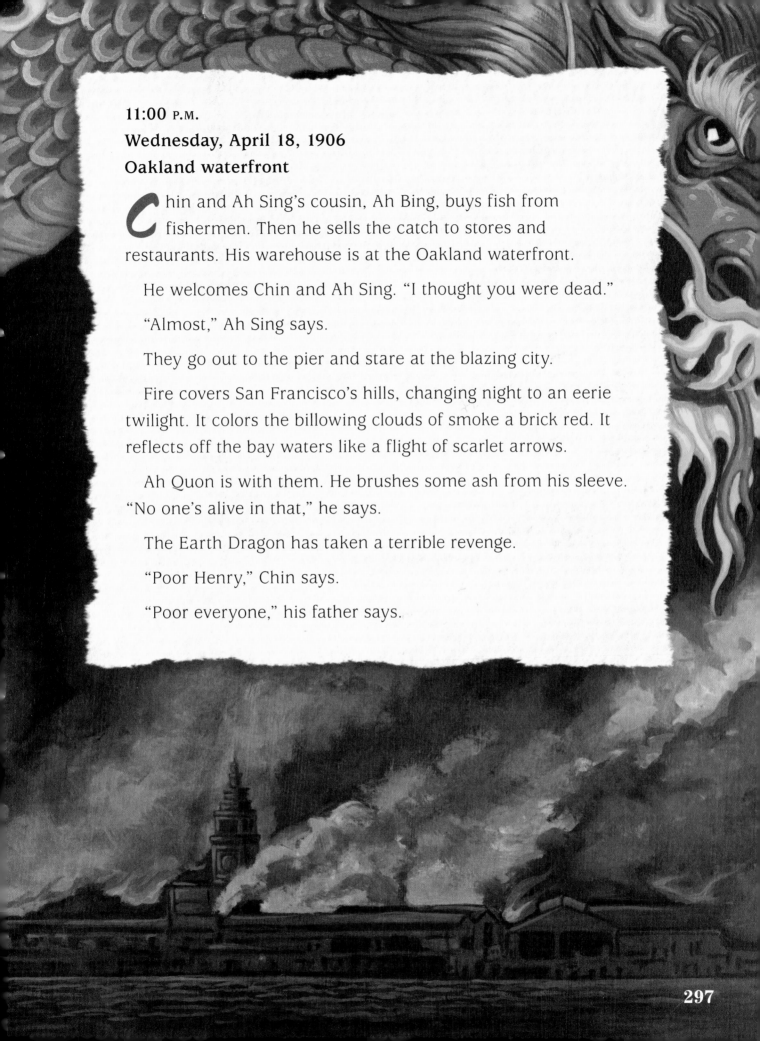

11:00 P.M.
Wednesday, April 18, 1906
Oakland waterfront

Chin and Ah Sing's cousin, Ah Bing, buys fish from fishermen. Then he sells the catch to stores and restaurants. His warehouse is at the Oakland waterfront.

He welcomes Chin and Ah Sing. "I thought you were dead."

"Almost," Ah Sing says.

They go out to the pier and stare at the blazing city.

Fire covers San Francisco's hills, changing night to an eerie twilight. It colors the billowing clouds of smoke a brick red. It reflects off the bay waters like a flight of scarlet arrows.

Ah Quon is with them. He brushes some ash from his sleeve. "No one's alive in that," he says.

The Earth Dragon has taken a terrible revenge.

"Poor Henry," Chin says.

"Poor everyone," his father says.

Meet the Author

Laurence Yep

Yep was born in San Francisco, California. His Chinese American family lived in an African American section of the city, so he had to commute to a bilingual school in Chinatown. Yep says that he never encountered white culture in America until high school and that he always felt like an outsider. Growing up, he found few books that dealt with being a Chinese American. Because of this, he uses his writing to fight racial stereotypes. He likes to write about this feeling of being an outsider and believes that this is the reason he is so popular with young adult readers.

Meet the Illustrator

Scott Goto

Goto has always wanted to be an artist. People and animals are among his favorite things to draw. Goto says that making fun and interesting characters come alive on the page is the best part of his job as an artist. He advises young artists to keep an open mind and to practice their craft to become better.

CALIFORNIA

SCIENCE: EARTH SCIENCES 5.a. Students know some changes in the earth are due to slow processes, such as erosion, and some changes are due to rapid processes, such as landslides, volcanic eruptions, and earthquakes.

Theme Connections

Discuss

Within the Selection

1. How does "The Earth Dragon Awakes" relate to the theme A Changing State?

2. How do Ah Sing and his son Chin survive the earthquake?

Across Selections

3. How is Chin's and Ah Sing's struggle to survive similar to another selection you have read in this unit?

4. Contrast the San Francisco of "Striking It Rich: The Story of the California Gold Rush" with the San Francisco seen in "The Earth Dragon Awakes."

Beyond the Selection

5. What did the 1906 earthquake teach people about cities and natural disasters?

6. How might people have learned from the 1906 earthquake?

Write

Imagine that a natural disaster struck a neighboring town. What could you do to help the people?

Read

Find magazine or newspaper articles about other natural disasters that have affected California in the past.

CALIFORNIA

SCIENCE: EARTH SCIENCES
5.a. Students know some
changes in the earth are
due to slow processes, such
as erosion, and some changes are due
to rapid processes, such as landslides,
volcanic eruptions, and earthquakes.

Science Link

Earthquakes and Volcanoes

Earth's land surface is shaped by slow processes such as erosion, but other changes are due to rapid processes such as volcanic eruptions and earthquakes.

Volcanoes

A volcano is a mountain that has an opening that allows rock and gases to escape. When pressure builds, eruptions occur, shooting out rock, ash, and billowing smoke. Volcanic eruptions can be so powerful that they clear entire forests in seconds. Active volcanoes in the U.S. are found mainly in Hawaii, Alaska, California, Oregon, and Washington. California is home to Lassen Peak, the southernmost active volcano in the Cascade Range. On May 22, 1915, Lassen Peak erupted, destroying a three-square-mile area in seconds. It last erupted in 1917.

Earthquakes

An earthquake occurs when two plates below Earth's surface suddenly slip past each other. The surface where they slip is called a fault. California has many fault lines, which means that it has more places where earthquakes are likely to occur. Sometimes earthquakes are so small people cannot feel them. Other times, they are so forceful that they can destroy entire cities.

Genre

Expository Text tells people something. It contains facts about real people, things, or events.

Text Feature

Time Lines show the order in which important events happened.

Think Link

On January 17, 1994, a large earthquake occurred in Northridge, California. The quake was felt for 2,000 square miles in Los Angeles, Orange, and Ventura counties. It killed fifty-seven people and injured nearly 12,000 people. About 100,000 houses and businesses were damaged, and some apartment buildings were reduced to rubble. The earthquake caused more than $40 billion in damage.

Major Earthquakes in California

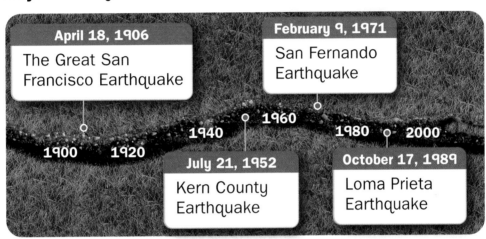

April 18, 1906
The Great San Francisco Earthquake

February 9, 1971
San Fernando Earthquake

1900   1920   1940   1960   1980   2000

July 21, 1952
Kern County Earthquake

October 17, 1989
Loma Prieta Earthquake

1. Which earthquake occurred closest to the time of Lassen Peak's eruption?

2. How do earthquakes and volcanoes affect the land's surface?

3. Why might earthquakes be uncommon elsewhere in the United States?

WebLink

CALIFORNIA

Visit **www.ImagineItReading.com/ AtHome** for more information about earthquakes and volcanoes in California.

Apply

Time Lines As you work on your investigation, think about how time lines can help show the order in which events occur.

CALIFORNIA

READING: VOCABULARY
AND CONCEPT
DEVELOPMENT 1.3 Use
knowledge of root words to
determine the meaning of unknown
words within a passage.

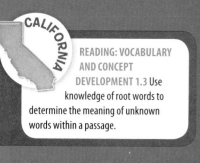

IN AND AROUND
Los
Angeles

Read the letter to find the meanings of these words, which are also in "In and Around Los Angeles":

✦ expedition
✦ magnitude
✦ beacon
✦ irresistibly
✦ lure
✦ descendants
✦ boasts
✦ flanked
✦ virtual
✦ clichés
✦ distill
✦ reliable

Vocabulary Development

Context Clues are hints in the text that help you find the meanings of words. Use context clues to find the meanings of *magnitude* and *beacon*.

Vocabulary
Warm-Up

Dear Mom and Dad,

I am having a great time on my trip to San Francisco. There are so many things to see and do. Today my expedition decided to take a boat ride through the bay to pass under the Golden Gate Bridge. Its magnitude surprised me when I got up close. It's huge! We headed back to shore after sunset. Our captain explained that he uses the beacon in the lighthouse to find his way back when it is dark.

When we reached land, I was starving. The aroma of sourdough bread and lobster bisque was irresistibly delicious. A small bakery managed to lure us in with the scent of freshly baked loaves. The owner told us stories about the city and how he and his family were descendants of the original settlers of California. I enjoyed listening to his accounts, although he boasts a little too much about his family's high status in the community.

After dinner we noticed a shop that flanked the bakery, so we stepped inside. It was a virtual tourist trap. The walls were covered with souvenirs, from snow globes of the city to postcards and key chains with clichés such as: "The coldest winter I ever spent was a summer in San Francisco." There were even little picture books that tried to distill the entire history of San Francisco in only a few pages.

We took a trolley ride back to the hotel. Tomorrow we are going to take a tour of the city. We found a guide from a tourist agency who is going to show us around. I'm so glad that I brought a reliable camera, because I want to make sure I get plenty of pictures. Well, I have a big day ahead, so I should get some rest. I'll see you in a few days!

Sincerely,

Kelly

Vocabulary Word Web

Work in a group of three. On a sheet of paper, have one person write a vocabulary word in the middle box. The second group member will think of a specific example of the word and write it in the diamond. The third member will think of a general example of the word and write it in the oval. Complete a word web for each word.

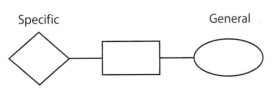

Specific   General

Concept Vocabulary

This lesson's concept word is **mosaic**. A *mosaic* is a picture or design made by fitting together colorful bits of stone, glass, or tile and cementing them in place. How might a place be a mosaic of culture? Can some places be more like a mosaic than others? How do you think Los Angeles is like a mosaic?

READING:
COMPREHENSION AND
ANALYSIS OF GRADE-
LEVEL-APPROPRIATE TEXT

2.2 Use appropriate strategies when reading for different purposes (e.g., full comprehension, location of information, personal enjoyment).

Genre

Expository Text tells people something. It contains facts about real people, things, or events.

Comprehension Skill

 Adjusting Reading Speed

As you read, notice where you are having trouble understanding the text, and decrease your reading speed. Also notice where you can increase your speed without losing comprehension.

IN AND AROUND
Los Angeles

by Julie Jaskol and Brian Lewis

Focus Questions

What different kinds of changes have affected Los Angeles and its neighbors? What are some of Los Angeles' biggest contributions to the world?

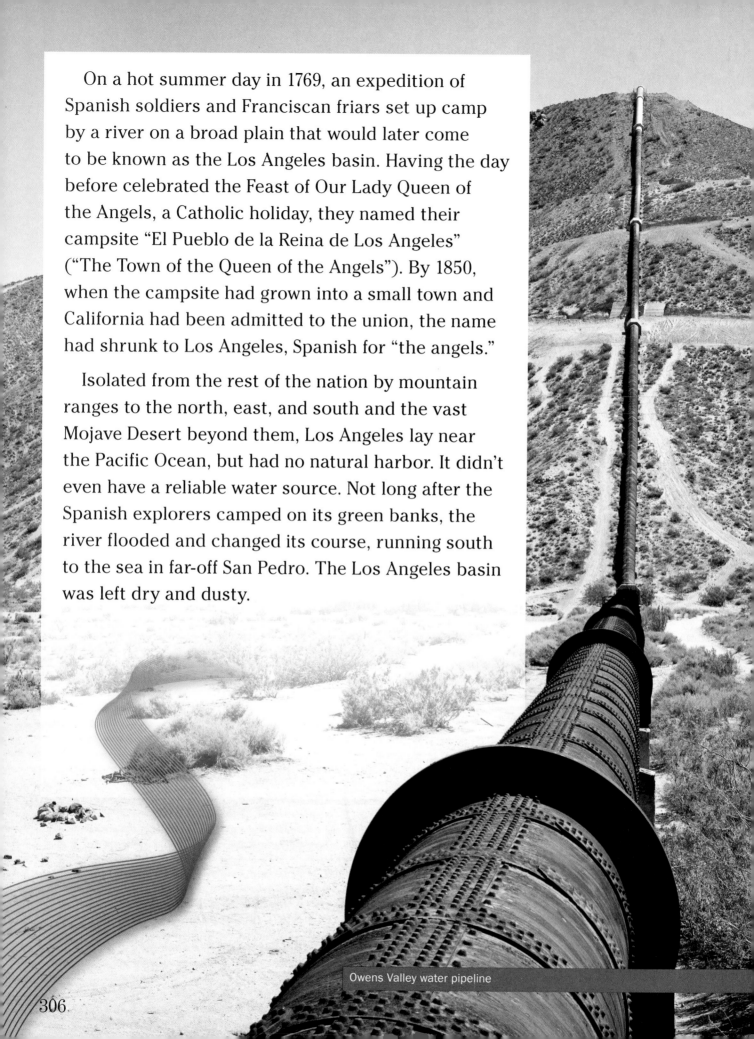

On a hot summer day in 1769, an expedition of Spanish soldiers and Franciscan friars set up camp by a river on a broad plain that would later come to be known as the Los Angeles basin. Having the day before celebrated the Feast of Our Lady Queen of the Angels, a Catholic holiday, they named their campsite "El Pueblo de la Reina de Los Angeles" ("The Town of the Queen of the Angels"). By 1850, when the campsite had grown into a small town and California had been admitted to the union, the name had shrunk to Los Angeles, Spanish for "the angels."

Isolated from the rest of the nation by mountain ranges to the north, east, and south and the vast Mojave Desert beyond them, Los Angeles lay near the Pacific Ocean, but had no natural harbor. It didn't even have a reliable water source. Not long after the Spanish explorers camped on its green banks, the river flooded and changed its course, running south to the sea in far-off San Pedro. The Los Angeles basin was left dry and dusty.

Owens Valley water pipeline

Los Angeles, 1950

Yet a city grew because people determinedly remade the land. By the early 20th century, railroads linked Los Angeles to the rest of the nation; a port connected it to the rest of the world; and a pipeline from Owens Valley in the north supplied a steady flow of water. Los Angeles' balmy climate and the vast possibilities of its wide open spaces irresistibly pulled people from older, colder cities back east, and from other countries as well.

Expanding without the rigid grids of planned communities, Los Angeles sprawled this way and that, eventually stretching some 465 square miles, gobbling up smaller cities in its path. Pasadena, Beverly Hills, and Santa Monica managed to keep their independent city councils and city halls, but Hollywood, Venice, and other smaller towns became neighborhoods in L.A. Today nearly 4 million residents make it the second largest city in the U.S. The city of Los Angeles is contained within Los Angeles County, which covers more than 4,000 square miles, and consists of 88 separate cities and more than 9 million people. The region boasts the world's highest rate of immigration, particularly from Asia and Latin America.

Streets change their character from block to block in L.A. Teeming, densely packed neighborhoods can quickly give way to quiet, lush areas where huge homes hide behind tall hedges. Storefront signs in Armenian dissolve into signs in Korean or Thai. Mediterranean-style houses with red-tiled roofs are flanked by English country cottages and L.A.'s unique "dingbat" apartment buildings, little more than boxes on stilts.

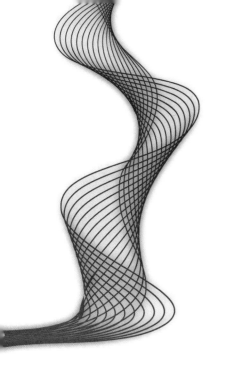

Some people sum up the city in easy-to-grasp clichés: convertibles, palm trees, cell phones; or, alternatively, earthquakes, riots, and annual brush fires that threaten to wipe Los Angeles off its canyons and hillsides. Writers have long tried to distill Los Angeles. Humorist Dorothy Parker sniffed dismissively that "Los Angeles is 72 suburbs in search of a city." Historian Carey McWilliams said it was like "a ringside seat at the circus." Novelist Raymond Chandler declared, "Los Angeles was just a big dry sunny place with ugly homes and no style, but good-hearted and peaceful."

Brush fire in Los Angeles

More about L.A. People and Places

Monument dedicated to explorer Juan Cabrillo

1542 Explorer Juan Cabrillo sails into San Pedro Bay and notices a layer of smoke from Native American campfires hanging over the land. He names the area "Bay of Smokes." His is the first account of the effects of the "inversion layer," warm air that sits like a lid on top of the Los Angeles basin, preventing pollution from blowing away.

1769 Father Juan Crespi, on the initial Spanish expedition to what will become Los Angeles, writes the first account of an L.A. earthquake, which knocked a soldier off his horse and "lasted as long as half an Ave Maria."

1851 A young African-American slave named Biddy Mason is brought by her owners to Los Angeles, where slavery is illegal. (California entered the Union as a free state in 1850.) She wins freedom for her family in court and, using her wages as a nurse and midwife to acquire property, goes on to become a major downtown landowner. In 1872, she helps organize the First African Methodist Episcopal Church, the oldest African-American church in the city. Today a small park on the Spring Street site of her home honors Biddy Mason's memory.

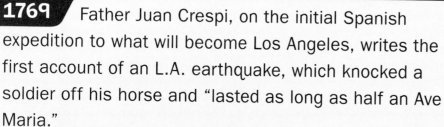

Charles Fletcher Lummis

Los Angeles Aqueduct

1884 Writer Charles Lummis walks all the way from Cincinnati, Ohio, to Los Angeles, where he becomes city editor of the *Los Angeles Times* and later the city librarian. His enthusiastic writings lure other artists and writers to Los Angeles. He establishes the California Landmarks Club to preserve L.A.'s historic buildings and helps found the Southwest Museum in Highland Park to study the region's native cultures. He builds a stone house with his own hands, which now serves at headquarters for the Historical Society of Southern California.

1887 Los Angeles finds itself in the midst of a boom. Railroads lower fares to a dollar for a transcontinental trip to L.A. Real-estate developers tout the healthful advantages of Los Angeles' climate.

1892 Edward Doheny strikes oil, launching another major boom in L.A. Drilling rigs sprout up throughout the region, with some areas of the city becoming virtual boomtowns. The substance that trapped Ice Age mammals 40,000 years ago creates fortunes for tycoons and for average people who find themselves lucky enough to live in the middle of an oil field.

1909 L.A.'s first movie studios are built in the Echo Park neighborhood. Soon the Keystone Kops, the Bathing Beauties, and Laurel & Hardy film their antics outside, transforming the community of Echo Park into a huge slapstick movie set.

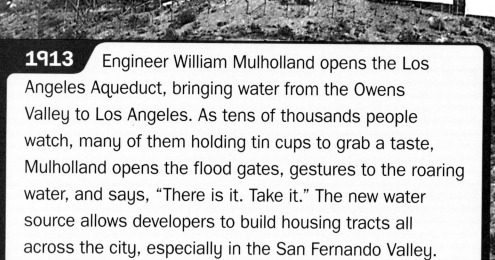

1913 Engineer William Mulholland opens the Los Angeles Aqueduct, bringing water from the Owens Valley to Los Angeles. As tens of thousands people watch, many of them holding tin cups to grab a taste, Mulholland opens the flood gates, gestures to the roaring water, and says, "There is it. Take it." The new water source allows developers to build housing tracts all across the city, especially in the San Fernando Valley.

1920 The movie industry takes over Hollywood. Dozens of studios operate on Sunset Boulevard near Gower Street. Cowboys line up at the corner, hoping for roles in Westerns, and the area becomes known as Gower Gulch. There's no holly to speak of in Hollywood. The name struck the fancy of Harvey Wilcox's wife after she met a woman on a train who had a summer home named "Hollywood." Wilcox owned the land that became Hollywood.

1921 Simon Rodia begins building Watts Towers. He offers neighborhood children a penny for every piece of broken crockery they bring him, until parents complain that their children are deliberately breaking dishes to earn money.

Los Angeles City Hall

1924 A film crew brings 14 buffalo to Catalina Island to recreate the American plains for a western movie. The crew leaves the buffalo behind. Today hundreds of their descendants roam the island's protected wilderness area.

1926 Christine Sterling launches a campaign to preserve Olvera Street, and the Chief of Police allows her to use prison work gangs. "One of the prisoners is a good carpenter, another an electrician. Each night I pray they will arrest a bricklayer and a plumber," she writes in her diary.

1928 Los Angeles' City Hall opens. The tallest building in downtown, its unprecedented 28 stories dwarf everything around it. At the top, a revolving light called the Charles Lindbergh Beacon warns off low-flying planes. Today, dozens of skyscrapers tower over City Hall, the tallest reaching 73 stories.

1932 Los Angeles hosts the Summer Olympics in the Los Angeles Memorial Coliseum, newly enlarged for the occasion to seat 105,000 people. Country Club Drive becomes Olympic Boulevard in time for the event, which brings 400,000 visitors and $50 million to the city.

1933 On March 10, just before 6 P.M., a major earthquake strikes, killing more than 100 people in the heavily populated areas of Long Beach, Garden Grove, Torrance, and Compton, south of L.A. It is the first earthquake for many newcomers—but not the last. The L.A. region experiences dozens of earthquakes a day, most of them too small to feel.

1935 Soon after the Griffith Observatory opens, a monkey escapes from the nearby zoo and climbs onto a model of the moon in the observatory's Hall of Science. It takes three hours, distinguished scientists, and a bunch of bananas to coax the monkey down from its perch and return the moon to its orbit. Afterward, the observatory's director says, "Don't tell me now there's not life on the moon."

1951 "This is the city," intones Jack Webb at the beginning of every episode of "Dragnet," a popular TV show based on actual cases from the Los Angeles Police Department. Airing until 1959, "Dragnet" returns eight years later for a three-year run in color.

1958 The Brooklyn Dodgers relocate to Los Angeles, bringing with them announcer Vin Scully, whose voice becomes the soundtrack to summer afternoons for generations of Angelenos. He begins each game with "A very pleasant good afternoon to you, wherever you may be...."

Griffith Observatory

1961 The last Red Car stops running, ending the era. The Red Car trolleys had traveled on tracks throughout the L.A. area since the turn of the century, at a cost of about a penny a mile. Increasing traffic and the efforts of auto, tire, and petroleum companies usher in the age of the freeway.

1962 Dodger Stadium opens in Chavez Ravine, on April 10, with a team that includes future baseball legends Sandy Koufax, Don Drysdale, and Maury Wills. In 1963, they win the World Series.

1973 Tom Bradley becomes L.A.'s first African-American mayor. He will lead the city for the next 20 years. During his five terms in office, the city will develop a major skyline and emerge as the leading trading partner with the Pacific Rim.

1984 Los Angeles becomes the first American city to host two Olympics. The 1984 Summer Olympic Games are considered by many to be Mayor Bradley's finest hour, as L.A. stages a profitable, peaceful, well-organized event. In fact, because of efforts to organize carpools and flexible work hours, traffic flows better during the Olympics than ever before—or since.

1994 On January 17 at 4:31 A.M., the Northridge earthquake strikes with a magnitude of 6.8, killing more than 60 people, injuring more than 6,000 others, and destroying or seriously damaging more than 1,000 buildings. Freeway overpasses collapse and more than 20,000 people lose their homes. It is one of the costliest disasters in American history.

Julie Jaskol and Brian Lewis

A husband-and-wife writing team, Jaskol and Lewis enjoy writing about their travels and experiences in and around Los Angeles. They met while they were reporters for the Los Angeles Independent Newspapers, which is a group of newspapers that have reported on the many different neighborhoods in Los Angeles for more than seventy-five years. They enjoy spending time with their children and sharing with the world their lifelong interest in the wonders of Los Angeles.

HISTORY-SOCIAL SCIENCE 4.4.4 Describe rapid American immigration, internal migration, settlement, and the growth of towns and cities (e.g., Los Angeles).

Theme Connections

Discuss

Within the Selection

1. What are some events in the history of Los Angeles that surprised you?

2. In what ways has Los Angeles changed over time? Explain your answers.

Across Selections

3. How is the influence of Spanish explorers on Los Angeles similar to what you have read previously in "The First Californians"?

4. Can you make any comparisons between the growth of Los Angeles and San Francisco during the Gold Rush?

Beyond the Selection

5. What contributions or influences have Los Angelenos made that directly affect you today?

6. Why do you think Los Angeles has a diverse culture?

Write

Imagine that a natural disaster struck a neighboring town. What could you do to help the people?

Read

Find magazine or newspaper articles about other natural disasters that have affected California in the past.

317

CALIFORNIA

HISTORY-SOCIAL SCIENCE
4.5.4 Explain the structures
and functions of state
governments, including the
roles and responsibilities of their elected
officials.

Social Studies Link

California's Elected Officials

Genre

Expository Text tells people something. It contains facts about real people, things, or events.

Text Feature

Charts present information in an organized and visual way.

Under the 10th Amendment to the U.S. Constitution, all governmental powers not granted to the federal government belong to the states. Each state has its own constitutions and three-branch governments modeled on the federal government. Each branch varies in magnitude and has its own powers and responsibilities.

The executive branch of every state is headed by an elected governor. The governor has the power to sign or veto laws, appoint judges, command the state military, and grant pardons for crimes. Most states also have a lieutenant governor. In California, the lieutenant governor is also the president of the California Senate. He or she must be reliable in case the governor is unable to carry out his or her duties.

The legislative branch in California has the Senate and the State Assembly. Its members are elected. They have the power to make laws, raise taxes, and adopt a state budget. The legislative branch can approve or reject many appointments made by the governor.

The judicial branch contains a system of courts. The courts interpret laws, make decisions about legal issues, and determine whether laws are being fairly enforced. Most judges are not elected by the people but are appointed by the governor.

Think Link

California's State Government

	Executive Branch	Legislative Branch	Judicial Branch
OFFICIALS	Governor, Lieutenant Governor	Members of the Senate and State Assembly	Judges
RESPONSIBILITIES	• Sign or veto laws • Appoint judges • Propose a budget • Give the State of the State Address • Command the state military • Grant pardons for crimes	• Make laws • Raise taxes • Adopt a budget • Approve or reject appointments	• Interpret the law • Make decisions concerning legal issues

1. The chart lists the three branches with their major officials and responsibilities. How does a chart make information easier to understand?

2. Who are the current officials in your state? Where can you find this information?

3. Why do you think there are three branches of government? How do they affect one another?

WebLink

Visit **www.ImagineItReading.com/ AtHome** for more information about elected officials in California.

Apply

Charts As you work on your investigation, think about how charts can present information in an organized and visual way.

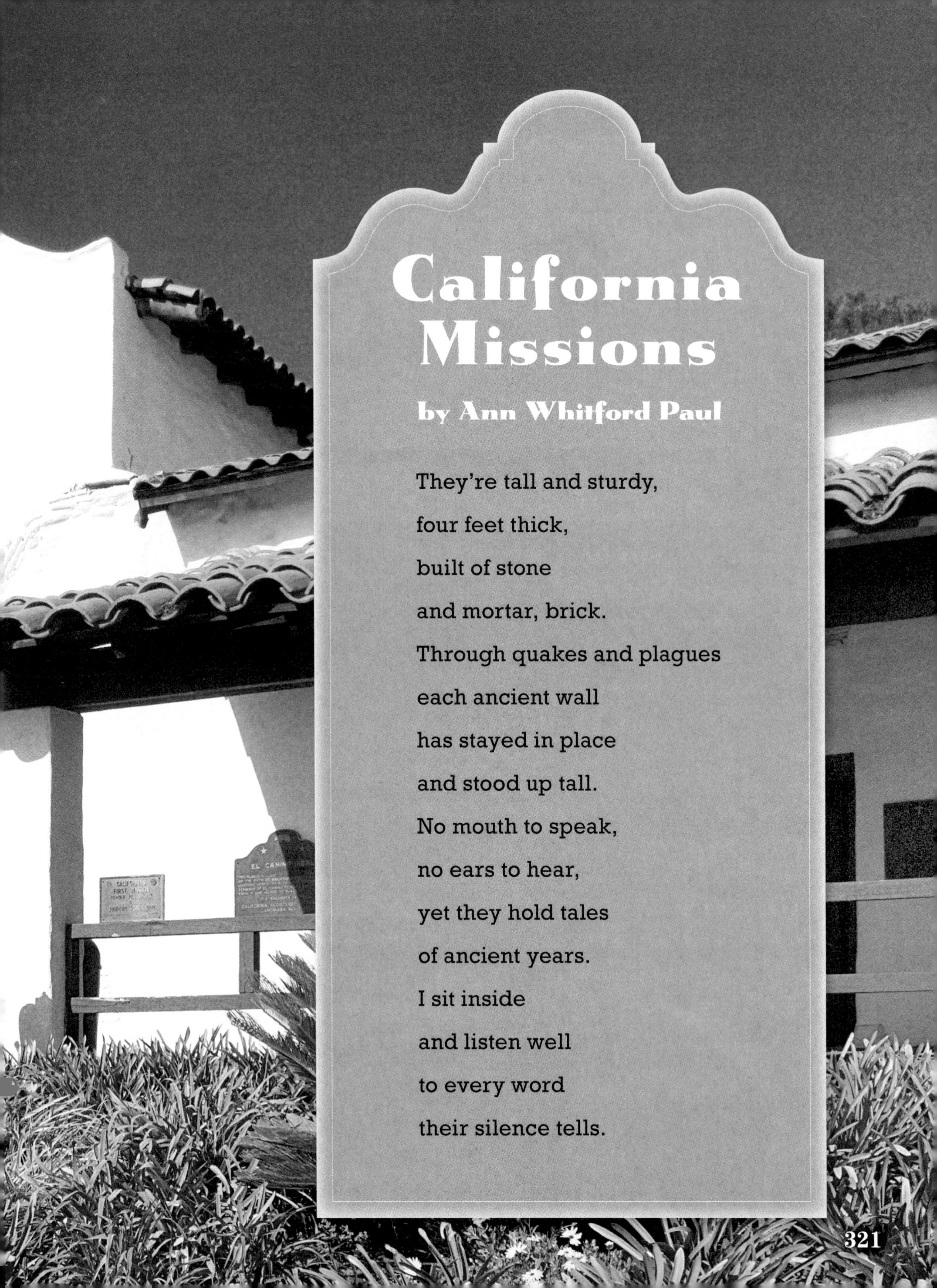

California Missions

by Ann Whitford Paul

They're tall and sturdy,

four feet thick,

built of stone

and mortar, brick.

Through quakes and plagues

each ancient wall

has stayed in place

and stood up tall.

No mouth to speak,

no ears to hear,

yet they hold tales

of ancient years.

I sit inside

and listen well

to every word

their silence tells.

Focus Questions As times change, what are some
things that remain the same? What happened to
people who did not "strike it rich"?

A Gold Miner's Tale

Written by Bobbi Katz   Illustrated by Troy Howell

Frank Wexler   Dawson City, Yukon Territory, 1898

I was twenty-one years old.
Fired up by dreams of gold.
Rushing West in '49
to stake a claim to my own mine!
What did I find when I got there?
Thousands of "rushers" everywhere!
Water and sand. That's ALL it takes.
Swish your pan. Pick out the flakes!

A meal?
A horse?
A place to stay?
Who'd believe what we had to pay!

Bought a shovel. Bought a pan.
Soon I'd be a rich young man.
Water and sand. That's ALL it takes.
Swish your pan. Pick out the flakes!
Pan after pan, I'd swish and wish
for a glint of pay dirt in my dish.
Asleep at night, what did I see?
Nuggets the daylight hid from me.
It takes more than a flash in the pan
to make a rusher a rich young man.

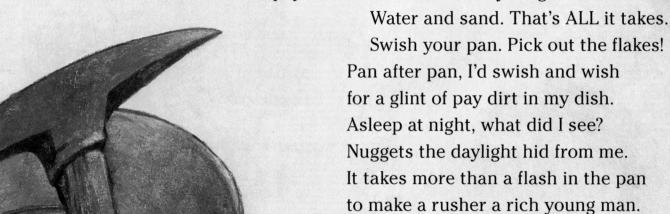

The gold I found? Just enough to get by.
I gave up when my claim went dry.
     Water and sand. That's ALL it takes.
     Swish your pan. Pick out the flakes!
Got a job in a hydraulic mine.
Hated the work, but the pay was fine.
So when I heard about Pikes Peak,
   I
     was
        in
            the Rockies
                 within a week!

     Water and sand. That's ALL it takes.
     Swish your pan. Pick out the flakes!
I should have known better.
     With a grubstake so small,
     I left Colorado with nothing at all.
No job. No gold. Just a shovel and a pan.
     But I walked away a wiser man.

"Gold in the Klondike!"
     Wouldn't you think
  I'd be up there in a wink?
But with my new plan to pan gold flakes,
I didn't make the same mistakes.
Before I joined the great stampede,
I thought: What will stampeders need?
Now I'm a Dawson millionaire!
I sell them ALL long underwear.

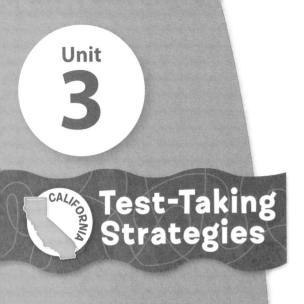

Test-Taking Strategies

Test-Taking Strategy: Comparing Answer Choices and Eliminating Answer Choices

Make sure you look at all the answer choices for each question. Compare the answers to one another. Choose the answer you think is best.

Comparing Answer Choices

You should carefully look at each answer on a test. It is easy to skip an answer choice or to misunderstand what it means. Think about what the question is asking. Compare the answer choices. Choose the answer that is best.

Read the sentences and the answer choices. What does the word *dreadful* mean? Make sure you read all the answer choices carefully. Decide which answer means the same as *dreadful*.

> **1. The weather was *dreadful*. It was cold, rainy, and windy.**
>
>   **A** pleasant
>
>   **B** changing
>
>   **C** terrible
>
>   **D** snowy

Compare the answer choices, and think about the sentences. Only one answer tells about cold, rainy, and windy weather. The word that best describes this kind of weather is *terrible*. The answer is **C**.

Sometimes you can eliminate answers that you know are not correct. For example, the first answer choice is *pleasant*, which is another word for *nice*. You can eliminate this answer because the weather described is not *nice*.

Test-Taking Practice

Read the article "Getting Around." Then answer Numbers 1 through 4.

Stand on a street corner sometime. Watch the traffic pass. Cars, trucks, and buses hum along on paved roads. Today, people usually travel in cars or buses. Long ago, though, travel was different.

Before the United States was a country, travel was difficult. Roads were rough and full of holes. Rocks and tree stumps made roads bumpy. People rode in wagons pulled by horses or oxen. Often dirt paths were the only way to get between farms and towns. People had to walk or ride on horseback.

People who lived near water could use boats. Boats were faster than traveling along bumpy roads. Ships on the ocean used sails. Boats going downstream on rivers moved quickly. However, traveling upstream was difficult and took a long time.

Not everyone lived close to water, so people built canals. A canal is a river made by people. It takes a long time to build and costs a lot of money. After a canal is dug and flooded with water, boats can easily travel along a canal.

Travel changed when trains were invented. Big companies built railroads between towns. In the 1860s, a railroad across the entire country was completed. In a train, people could travel from coast to coast in a few days.

Automobiles were invented in the early 1900s. Cars made travel easier for people. Travelers could set their own schedules instead of waiting for trains. Better, smoother roads for cars were built across the country. Soon, cars were popular. By 1960, most families owned a car.

Today, millions of people travel by car. The old types of transportation still are around, though. Many people walk to get where they need to go. In some places, horse-drawn wagons are used, and boats are common. Trains still chug their way across the country.

One old-fashioned way of getting around—bicycling— is becoming popular again. Bicycles cost less than cars, create less pollution, and cause fewer traffic jams. Riding a bike is good exercise too. Now that roads are smoothly paved, riding a bicycle is easier. Considering how much gasoline costs today, it is likely that more people will start to travel by riding bicycles.

Use the information you learned from the article "Getting Around" to answer questions 1 through 4. Write your answers on a piece of paper.

Test Tips

- Use the information in the story to answer the questions.

- Compare the answer choices.

- Look in the story to find the answer to each question.

1. This selection is mainly about

    A why canals are important.

    B how roads were mostly dirt.

    C why bicycling is good.

    D forms of transportation.

2. Why did people build canals?

    A To avoid using sails

    B To make travel easier

    C To replace the railroads

    D To make roads smoother

3. Which statement would the author *most likely* agree with?

    A Canals were easy and quick to build.

    B Trains are more convenient than cars.

    C Travel long ago was slow and difficult.

    D Riding a bicycle is an unpleasant way to travel.

4. Which words from the article tell about an advantage of bicycling?

    A "create less pollution"

    B "expensive and hard to do"

    C "people had to travel"

    D "travel from coast to coast"

Pronunciation Key

a as in **a**t
ā as in l**a**te
â as in c**a**re
ä as in f**a**ther
e as in s**e**t
ē as in m**e**
i as in **i**t
ī as in k**i**te
o as in **o**x
ō as in r**o**se

ô as in b**ou**ght and r**a**w
oi as in c**oi**n
o͞o as in b**oo**k
o͞o as in t**oo**
or as in f**or**m
ou as in **ou**t
u as in **u**p
ū as in **u**se
ûr as in t**ur**n, g**er**m, l**ear**n, f**ir**m, w**or**k

ə as in **a**bout, chick**e**n, penc**i**l, cann**o**n, circ**u**s
ch as in **ch**air
hw as in **wh**ich
ng as in ri**ng**
sh as in **sh**op
th as in **th**in
t͟h as in **th**ere
zh as in trea**s**ure

The mark (ˊ) is placed after a syllable with a heavy accent, as in **chicken** (**chik**ˊ ən).

The mark (ˏ) after a syllable shows a lighter accent, as in **disappear** (**dis**ˊ ə pērˊ).

Glossary

abolitionist (ab´ ə lish´ ə nist) *n.* person who wanted to end slavery in the United States

abundance (ə bun´ dənts) *n.* a large amount

accounting (ə koun´ tīng) *n.* a system of tracking the finances for a business

acorns (ā´ kôrnz) *n.* plural of **acorn:** the nut of the oak tree

advance (ad vans´) *v.* to move forward; to help the progress or growth of

aftershock (af´ tər shäk) *n.* a small earthquake or tremor that follows a major earthquake

agitated (aj´ i tā tid´) *v.* past tense of **agitate:** to stir up or shake

alarmingly (ə lär´ ming lē) *adv.* in a frightening way

ancestors (an´ ses´ tərs) *n.* plural of **ancestor:** someone from long ago in a direct relation to you, for example a great-great-grandparent

ancient (ān´ shənt) *adj.* very old; relating to times long ago

Word History

The adjective *ancient* originally comes from the Latin word *ante*, meaning "before." This root was later changed as it passed through Middle English as *ancien*.

arc (ärk) *n.* a curved line between two points on a circle

aqueduct (ak´ wi dukt´) *n.* a large pipe or other channel that carries water over a long distance

associations (ə sō´ sē ā´ shəns) *n.* plural of **association:** a friendship or a connection

astonishment (ə ston´ ish mənt) *n.* great surprise; amazement

authoritative (ə thôr´ i tā´ tiv) *adj.* worthy of belief; reliable

Pronunciation Key: at; lāte; câre; fäther; set; mē; it; kīte; ox; rōse; ô in bought; coin; bŏŏk; tōō; form; out; up; ūse; tûrn; ə sound in about, chicken, pencil, cannon, circus; **ch**air; **hw** in **wh**ich; ri**ng**; **sh**op; **th**in; **th**ere; **zh** in trea**s**ure.

B

bacteria (bak tir´ ē ə) *n.* tiny living cells that can only be seen through a microscope—some bacteria can cause diseases, but others do useful things, such as making soil richer

balmy (bäl´ mē) *adj.* mild and refreshing

bark (bärk) *n.* the outer covering of the outside of a tree

beacon (bē´ kən) *n.* a light or other signal that warns or guides ships or aircraft

beds (bedz) *n.* plural of **bed:** a place where plants grow together

belong (bi long´) *v.* to fit into a group

billowing (bil´ ō ing) *v.* form of **billow:** to rise up in a large surging mass

biology (bī ol´ ə jē) *n.* the study of the way in which plants, animals, and other living things live and grow

bitterly (bi´ tər lē) *adv.* harshly; extremely

boasts (bōsts) *v.* form of **boast:** to talk too much or with too much pride about oneself; to brag

bow (bou) *n.* the front part of a ship

bow

branch (branch) *v.* to divide and subdivide

brilliant (bril´ yənt) *adj.* bright

brittle (bri´ təl) *adj.* easily broken

brook (brŏŏk) *n.* a small natural stream of fresh water

bureau (byŏŏr´ ō) *n.* a chest of drawers

burrow (bûr´ ō) *n.* a hole in the ground to live in

C

canopy (ka´ nə pē) *n.* the upper part of the rain forest

canteens (kan tēnz´) *n.* plural of **canteen:** a small metal container for carrying water to drink

capacity (kə pa´ sə tē) *n.* ability

captivity (kap ti´ və tē) *n.* the state of being a prisoner or held in confinement

ceded (sēd´ əd) *v.* past tense of **cede:** to surrender possession of

chafing (chā´ fing) *v.* form of **chafe:** to rub in a painful way

circulate (sûr´ kyə lāt) *v.* to flow around freely

circumstances (sûr´ kəm stants´ əz) *n.* plural of **circumstance:** the way things are at the moment

Word History

The word *circumstance* comes from a form of the Latin verb *circumstare,* "to stand around," which is formed from the prefix *circum-,* "around" and the verb *stare,* "to stand."

cisterns (sis´ tərnz) *n.* plural of **cistern:** A tank or container for storing or holding water

clichés (klē shāz´) *n.* plural of **cliché:** an overused expression or idea

climate (klī´ mət) *n.* the average weather conditions of a place over a period of years

clinging (kling´ ing) *v.* form of **cling:** to hold on tight

coal (kōl) *n.* a black mineral burned to make heat

cocoons (kə kōōnz´) *n.* plural of **cocoon:** the silky envelope spun by the larvae of insects to protect themselves during a phase of growth

comeback (kum´ bak) *n.* a return to a former position or condition

Pronunciation Key: at; l**ā**te; c**â**re; f**ä**ther; s**e**t; m**ē**; **i**t; k**ī**te; **o**x; r**ō**se; **ô** in b**ou**ght; c**oi**n; b**o͝o**k; t**o͞o**; f**o**rm; **ou**t; **u**p; **ū**se; t**û**rn; **ə** sound in **a**bout, chick**e**n, penc**i**l, cann**o**n, circ**u**s; **ch**air; **hw** in **wh**ich; ri**ng**; **sh**op; **th**in; **th**ere; **zh** in trea**s**ure.

companions (kəm pan´ yənz) *n.* plural of **companion:** a person who often goes along with another; friend; comrade

concealed (kən sēld´) *v.* past tense of **conceal:** to hide

concerned (kən sûrnd´) *adj.* showing worry

condensing (kən dens´ ing) *v.* form of **condense:** to make or become less in size or volume

conscience (kon´ shəns) *n.* a sense of right and wrong

consider (kən si´ dər) *v.* to think carefully about something before deciding

consoled (kən sōld´) *v.* past tense of **console:** to try to make someone feel better

contains (kən tānz´) *v.* form of **contain:** to hold

courtyards (kort´ yärdz) *n.* plural of **courtyard:** an open space exposed to the sky, especially one enclosed on all four sides

cover (ku´ vər) *n.* something that would be good to hide behind

creates (krē āts´) *v.* form of **create:** to make

Word Derivations

Below are some words derived from the word *create.*

creative	creativity	uncreated
creation	creator	creature
recreation	recreational	recreate

crockery (krä´ kə rē) *n.* earthenware; plates, dishes

crowed (krōd) *v.* past tense of **crow:** to brag loudly

crumpled (krum´ pəld) *v.* past tense of **crumple:** to press or crush into wrinkles

dabbed (dabd) *v.* past tense of **dab:** to gently apply a small amount of liquid

daggers (dag´ ərz) *n.* plural of **dagger:** a short sword-like weapon with a pointed blade and a handle

dangle (dang´ gəl) *v.* to hang; to swing loosely

dappled (da´ pəld) *adj.* having spots

daubed (dôbd) *v.* past tense of **daub:** to smear

debris (də brē´) *n.* the remains of anything broken down or destroyed

decays (di kāz´) *v.* form of **decay:** to slowly break down

decent (dē´ sənt) *adj.* good enough to make someone comfortable

delectable (di lek´ tə bəl) *adj.* very pleasing to the taste

delivered (di li´ vərd) *v.* past tense of **deliver:** to save from danger

denomination (di nom´ ə nā´ shən) *n.* a religious group or sect

depend (di pend´) *v.* to need; to rely

descendants (di send´ ənts) *n.* plural of **descendant:** a person, animal, or plant whose descent can be traced to a particular individual or group

deserted (di zûr´ təd) *v.* past tense of **desert:** to leave; to abandon; *adj.* having no people

despairing (di spâr´ ing) *adj.* to be without hope

detained (di tānd´) *v.* form of **detain:** to keep back; to delay

determinedly (di tûr´ mind lē) *adv.* to be resolute, decided, or resolved

dilapidated (di lap´ i dā´ tid) *adj.* fallen into ruin or decay; broken down

dilemma (də le´ mə) *n.* a situation in which each choice looks equally bad

Word History

The noun *dilemma* comes from the Greek word *dilēmmatos*, meaning "involving two assumptions." The word was later altered in Late Greek to *dilēmma*. This last spelling closely resembles the modern English spelling.

disbanded (dis band´ əd) *v.* past tense of **disband:** to break up

dismissively (dis mis´ iv lē) *adv.* indicating dismissal or rejection; disdainful

dispute (dis pūt´) *n.* an argument or conflict

distill (di´ stil) *v.* to condense; to make simpler

distract (di strakt´) *v.* to draw attention away from what someone is doing

domain (dō mān´) *n.* a territory governed by a single ruler

dormitory (dôr´ mi tôr´ ē) *n.* a building in which there are many bedrooms

dozed (dōzd) *v.* past tense of **doze:** to sleep lightly

Pronunciation Key: at; lāte; câre; fäther; set; mē; it; kīte; ox; rōse; ô in bought; coin; bŏŏk; tŏŏ; form; out; up; ūse; tûrn; ə sound in about, chicken, pencil, cannon, circus; chair; hw in which; ring; shop; thin; there; zh in treasure.

drooping (drŏŏp´ ing) *v.* form of **droop:** to hang or sink down; to sag

droplet (dräp´ lət) *n.* a tiny drop of liquid

earnestly (ûr´ nəst lē) *adj.* seriously; with importance

earthquake (ûrth´ kwāk) *n.* a shaking of the Earth´s surface caused by shifting plates in the Earth´s crust

ecosystem (ē´ kō sis´ təm) *n.* all living and nonliving things in a certain area that are linked together

eerie (ir´ ē) *adj.* strange and frightening

elegant (e´ li gənt) *adj.* rich and fine in quality

emigrants (em´ i grənts) *n.* plural of **emigrant:** a person who leaves his or her own country to live in another

enclosed (in klōzd´) *v.* past tense of **enclose:** to set inside

energy (e´ nər jē) *n.* the power to do work

engaged (in gājd´) *adj.* busy; occupied

enrich (en rich´) *v.* to improve or make better by adding something

epidemics (ep´ə dem´ iks) *n.* plural of **epidemic:** an outbreak of a contagious disease

escorted (es kor´ təd) *v.* past tense of **escort:** to go along with; to accompany

evaporated (i va´ pə rā´ təd) *v.* past tense of **evaporate:** to change from liquid to gas

Word History

The Latin *evaporare,* "to disperse in steam," is formed from the prefix *ex-,* "from" and the root *vapor,* "steam." This came into English as *evaporate.*

eventually (i vent´ shə wə lē) *adv.* sooner or later

expedition (ek´ spi dish´ ən) *n.* a group of people making a journey

exploration (ek´ splə rā´ shən) *n.* travel for the purpose of discovery

F

faint (fānt) *adj.* weak; very low

farmhand (farm hand) *n.* a worker on a farm

feast (fēst) *v.* to eat

ferried (fâr´ ēd) *v.* past tense of **ferry:** to bring across on a boat

fiber (fī´ bər) *n.* a piece of cloth

Word Derivations

Below are some words derived from the word *fiber.*

fiberboard	fiberglass	fiber optics
fiberfill	fiberize	fibers
fibered	fiber-optic	fiberscope

figure (fi´ gyûr) *n.* shape

filters (fil´ tərz) *n.* plural of **filter:** a device with tiny holes, designed to strain out dirt as a liquid or gas goes through

flanked (flangkd) *v.* form of **flank:** to be at the side of

flickering (fli´ kər ing) *adj.* becoming brighter and then darker over and over

flowed (flōd) *v.* past tense of **flow:** to move as water does

fluttered (flut´ ərd) *v.* past tense of **flutter:** to move or fly with quick, light, flapping movements

food chain (fo͞od´ chān) *n.* a series of living things, in which the first is eaten by the second, the second is eaten by the third, and so on

food web (fo͞od´ web) *n.* a complex system of food chains

forehead (fôr´ hed´) *n.* the part of the face above the eyebrows and below the hairline

fortunate (for´ chə nit) *adj.* having or resulting from good luck; lucky

fortune (for´ chən) *n.* luck

fossil fuel (fä´ səl fū´ əl) *n.* a fuel formed from the remains of ancient plants and animals

fossilized (fä´ sə lī zəd) *v.* past tense of **fossilize:** to become preserved and hardened in rock

fragrant (frā´ grənt) *adj.* sweet smelling

fuels (fū´ əlz) *n.* plural of **fuel:** something that gives out energy as it is burned

furiously (fyo͞or´ ē əs lē) *adv.* with great energy

Pronunciation Key: at; lāte; câre; fäther; set; mē; it; kīte; ox; rōse; ô in bought; coin; bŏŏk; tōō; form; out; up; ūse; tûrn; ə sound in about, chicken, pencil, cannon, circus; **ch**air; **hw** in **wh**ich; ri**ng**; **sh**op; **th**in; **th**ere; **zh** in treasure.

G

gasoline (gas´ ə lēn) *n.* a clear liquid that burns easily—it is made of petroleum and is used as a fuel for cars, airplanes, and other vehicles

generations (je nə rā´ shənz) *n.* plural of **generation:** a group of people born around the same time

geologist (jē ä´ lə jist) *n.* a person who studies the history and development of the Earth as shown through rocks

glacier (glā´ shər) *n.* a huge mass of ice formed from snow, usually found in the polar regions or in high mountains

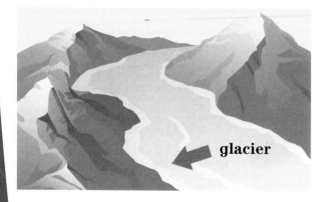

glacier

glumly (glum´ lē) *adv.* sadly and quietly

gold rush (gōld rush) *n.* a rush to newly discovered gold fields in an attempt to get rich

grazing (grā´ zing) *n.* opportunities for cattle to find grass to eat

griffins (gri´ fənz) *n.* plural of **griffin:** a winged monster with the head of an eagle and the body of a lion

guzzled (gə´ zəld) v. past tense of **guzzle:** to drink greedily or excessively

H

harbor (här´ bər) *n.* a sheltered place along a coast, where ships and boats often anchor

hardships (härd´ ships´) *n.* plural of **hardship:** something that causes difficulty, pain or suffering

harsh (härsh) *adj.* rough; cruel

hastened (hā´ sənd) *v.* past tense of **hasten:** to hurry

headland (həd´ lənd) *n.* a point of high land that sticks out into the water; cape

history (his´ tə rē) *n.* a chronological record of significant events

hoarse (hôrs) *adj.* having a weak or rough voice, often as a result of shouting

hollow (hä´ lō) *n.* a low spot

humbly (hum´ blē) *adv.* not proudly

Word History

The word *humble* traces back to the Latin word *humus*, "earth, soil." *Humbly* is formed by adding the suffix *-ly*, "in a certain way."

hurdle (hûr´ dəl) *n.* a barrier to be jumped over in a race; a difficulty or problem

hurtled (hûr´ təld) *v.* past tense of **hurtle:** to fall wildly

idly (īd´ lē) *adv.* not doing anything

impressed (im prest´) *v.* past tense of **impress:** to have a strong effect on the mind or feelings

ineffectively (i´ nə fek´ tiv lē) *adv.* without result

ingredients (in grē´ dē ənts) *n.* plural of **ingredient:** an item in a recipe

irrigation (ēr´ ə gā´ shən) *n.* having to do with supplying farmland with water.

Word History

The verb *irrigate* traces back to the Latin prefix *in-*, "into" and the verb *rigare*, "to make something wet." A later addition of the suffix *-tion*, which turns actions into nouns, produces the noun *irrigation*.

island (ī´ lənd) *n.* an area of land surrounded by water and smaller than a continent

isolated (ī´ sə lāt´ əd) *v.* past tense of **isolate:** to set apart or cut off from others

jagged (ja´ gəd) *adj.* having sharp points that stick out

jeered (jērd´) *v.* past tense of **jeer:** to abuse vocally; to taunt

judgment (juj´ mənt) *n.* an opinion or conclusion reached through reasoning

kneeling (nēl´ ing) *v.* form of **kneel:** to rest on one or both knees

Pronunciation Key: at; l**ā**te; c**â**re; f**ä**ther; s**e**t; m**ē**; **i**t; k**ī**te; **o**x; r**ō**se; **ô** in b**ou**ght; c**oi**n; b**oo**k; t**oo**; f**o**rm; **ou**t; **u**p; **ū**se; t**û**rn; **ə** sound in **a**bout, chick**e**n, penc**i**l, cann**o**n, circ**u**s; **ch**air; **hw** in **wh**ich; ri**ng**; **sh**op; **th**in; **t͟h**ere; **zh** in trea**s**ure.

krill (kril) *n.* shrimp-like sea creatures—a major source of food for whales

lacking (lak´ ing) *v.* form of **lack:** to be without

larva (lär´ və) *n.* a young insect that hatches from an egg and has a wormlike form before growing into an adult

ledger (lej´ ər) *n.* a book used for accounting

lessened (les´ ənd) *v.* past tense of **lessen:** to make or become less

liberty (li´ bər tē) *n.* the quality or state of being free

linked (linkt) *v.* past tense of **link:** to connect

liquefaction (li´ kwə fak´ shən) *n.* the conversion of a solid or gas into a liquid

litter (li´ tər) *n.* bits or scraps of paper or other rubbish; mess

lure (loor) *v.* to attract strongly

lush (lush) *adj.* thick, rich, and abundant

luxurious (lug´ zhoor´ ē əs) *adj.* rich and comfortable

magnitude (mag´ ni tood´) *n.* greatness of size

mastodons (mas´ tə dänz) *n.* plural of **mastodon:** an extinct, very large elephant-like mammal

measure (me´ zhər) *n.* an amount or degree of something

merriment (mâr´ i mənt) *n.* fun.

microbes (mī´ krōbz) *n.* plural of **microbe:** a very tiny living thing; a microorganism

microscope (mī´ krə skōp´) *n.* a tool for looking at very small things

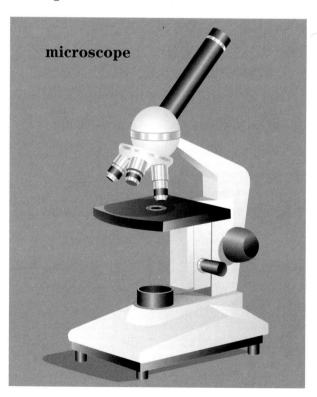

microscope

migration (mī grā´ shən) *n.* a large movement of people or animals from one place to another

miracles (mir´ ə kəlz) *n.* plural of **miracle:** an extremely outstanding or unusual event

miserable (mi´ zər bəl) *adj.* very unhappy

missionaries (mi´ shə ner´ ēz) *n.* plural of **missionary:** a person who is sent to teach and spread a particular religion

mold (mōld) *n.* a fuzzy-looking fungus that grows on damp surfaces

mortar (môr´ tər) *n.* a material used to bind together bricks or stones

mosaic (mō zā´ ik) *n.* a picture of design made by fitting together bits of stone, glass, or tile of different colors, and cementing them in place

Word History

Originally from the Latin word *museum*, meaning "a place where objects are exhibited," *mosaic* was derived from various Latin versions and the Middle English *musycke*.

movement (mōōv´ mənt) *n.* the act of moving; a tendency or trend

murmured (mûr´ mərd) *v.* past tense of **murmur:** a low, soft sound

nervously (nûr´ vəs lē) *adv.* uneasily

natural gas (na´ chə rəl gas´) *n.* a gas found beneath Earth´s surface that burns easily and steadily

nudged (nujd) *v.* past tense of **nudge:** to push slightly

O

obviously (ob´ vē əs lē) *adv.* in a way that is easy to see

officials (ə fi´ shəlz) *n.* plural of **official:** a person who holds an office

oil (oil) *n.* a liquid found beneath Earth´s surface that is commonly used as fuel and for many other uses; petroleum

omen (ō´ mən) *n.* a sign of something about to happen

opportunities (o´ pər tōō´ nə tēz) *n.* plural of **opportunity:** a chance to succeed in life

overlapping (ō´ vər la´ ping) *n.* the way something extends over something else

ownership (ōn´ ər ship) *n.* the state or fact of being an owner

Pronunciation Key: at; lāte; câre; fäther; set; mē; it; kīte; ox; rōse; ô in bought; coin; book; too; form; out; up; ūse; tûrn; ə sound in about, chicken, pencil, cannon, circus; chair; hw in which; ring; shop; thin; there; zh in treasure.

oxygen (ok´ si jən) *n.* a gas that makes up about one-fifth of Earth´s atmosphere and that animals must breathe to live

paleontologists (pā´ lē ən tol´ ə jists) *n.* plural of **paleontologist:** a person who studies fossils

pampas (pam´ pəz) *n.* plural of **pampa:** the vast grassy plains of South America

particles (pär´ ti kəlz) *n.* plural of **particle:** a tiny piece

peninsula (pə nin´ sə lə) *n.* an area of land that juts out from a larger area of land and is surrounded by water on three sides

Word History

Peninsula comes from the Latin roots *paene*, meaning "almost," and *insula*, meaning "island," with slight English spelling changes.

perilous (per´ əl əs) *adj.* involving or full of great risk of harm

permanent (pûr´ mə nənt) *adj.* lasting; not temporary

photosynthesis (fō´ tə sin´ thə sis) *n.* the process by which green plants combine carbon dioxide, water, and sunlight to produce food

pickpocket (pik´ pok´ it) *n.* a person who steals from other people´s pockets or purses

piracy (pī´ rə sē) *n.* robbery

pitch (pich) *v.* to set up

plodding (pläd´ ing) *adj.* form of **plod:** to move in a slow, heavy way

plume (ploom) *n.* a big fluffy feather

plump (plump) *adj.* having a full, rounded form

pollinate (pä´ lə nāt´) *v.* to spread pollen from flower to flower, allowing fruit and seeds to grow

posts (pōsts) *n.* plural of **post:** a place where a soldier or guard is ordered to be

practical (prak´ ti kəl) *adj.* concerned with ordinary activities, business, or work

prehistoric (prē´ his tor´ ik) *adj.* from very long ago, before people started writing history

preoccupied (prē ä´ kyə pīd´) *adj.* paying attention to something else

presidios (pri sē´ dē ōz´) *n.* plural of **presidio:** a fort or military post

preyed (prād) *v.* past tense of **prey:** to take advantage of; to cause harm to

process (prä´ ses´) *n.* a series of actions involved in making or doing something

prominent (prä´ mə nənt) *adj.* leading, important, well-known

provisions (prə vi´ zhənz) *n.* plural of **provision:** a supply of food and other necessary items

pursued (pər sōōd´) *v.* past tense of **pursue:** to chase

R

raging (rā´ jing) *adj.* violent; wild

recalled (ri käld´) *v.* past tense of **recall:** to remember

recurring (ri kər´ ing) *adj.* happening over and over

release (ri lēs´) *v.* to let loose

reliable (ri lī´ ə bəl) *adj.* able to be depended on and trusted

remains (ri mānz´) *n.* things that are left

Renaissance (ren´ ə säns´) *n.* a renewal or revival of something, especially in learning, art, and literature

Word History

Renaissance comes from the Latin prefix *re-* and Latin root *nasci,* meaning "to be born." The French altered the spelling to *renaistre* and gave it the meaning of "to be born again" or "rebirth."

replicas (rep´ li kəs) *n.* plural of **replica:** a close or exact copy

require (ri kwīr´) *v.* to have a need of

reservoir (re´ zə vwär´) *n.* a lake, often artificial, for storing water

resolute (rez´ uh lōōt) *adj.* marked by firm determination

rich (rich) *adj.* deep and full of health

roamed (rōmd) *v.* past tense of **roam:** to go from place to place without purpose or direction

roundabout (round´ ə bout´) *adj.* not straight or direct

rot (rot) *n.* a decay or breaking down of dead things

Pronunciation Key: at; lāte; câre; fäther; set; mē; it; kīte; ox; rōse; ô in bought; coin; bŏŏk; tōō; form; out; up; ūse; tûrn; ə sound in about, chicken, pencil, cannon, circus; chair; hw in which; ring; shop; thin; there; zh in treasure.

route (rōōt) *n.* a path or road

Word History

Route is from the Latin word *rupta*, meaning "broken way." The Anglo-French later altered the spelling to *rute*.

rubble (rub´ əl) *n.* the remains of something that has been destroyed or broken up

ruins (rōō´ ənz) *n.* plural of **ruin:** the remains of something destroyed or decayed

rumors (rōō´ mərz) *n.* plural of **rumor:** a story without proof that passes from person to person

rutabagas (rōō´ tə bā´ gəz) *n.* plural of **rutabaga:** a turnip that usually produces a large yellowish root that is eaten as a vegetable

S

sags (sagz) *v.* form of **sag:** to sink or hang down

sandspit (sand´ spit´) *n.* a narrow point of sand extending into a body of water

sawmill (sô´ mil) *n.* a place where machines saw logs into lumber

scarce (skârs) *adj.* hard to find

scatter (ska´ tər) *v.* to go or rush in different directions

scatterbrained (ska´ tər brānd´) *adj.* lacking sense, direction, or focus

scrabble (skra´ bəl) *v.* to scratch or dig frantically with the hands

seafloor (sē´ flôr) *n.* the bottom of a sea or ocean

seaweed (sē´ wēd) *n.* a plant that grows near the surface of the sea

seeping (sēp´ ing) *v.* form of **seep:** to flow or spread slowly

series (sēr´ ēz) *n.* several of something in a row

serpent (sûr´ pənt) *n.* a snake

sharp (shärp) *adj.* able to see details

sheepishly (shēp´ ish lē) *adv.* embarrassed or bashful

shone (shōn) *v.* past tense of **shine:** to give or reflect light

shrill (shril) *adj.* having a sharp high-pitched tone

shrivel (shri´ vəl) *v.* to wrinkle and become small

shuddered (shu´ dərd) *v.* past tense of **shudder:** to shake with horror

silvery (sil´ vər´ ē) *adj.* resembling silver; of a lustrous grayish-white color

slightly (slīt´ lē) *adv.* by a little bit

smoldering (smōl´ dər ing) *v.* form of **smolder:** to burn and smoke without flames

snatched (snacht) *v.* form of **snatch:** to grab

soar (sor) *v.* to fly high

softened (sô´ fən əd) *v.* past tense of **soften:** to become weak; to melt

spiny (spī´ nē) *adj.* covered with or having sharp points, as an animal

splinter (splin´ tər) *n.* a thin, sharp piece broken off from something hard or brittle

sprout (sprout) *v.* to begin to grow

squawking (skwôk´ ing) *v.* form of **squawk:** to utter a harsh, abrupt scream

stampede (stam pēd´) *v.* to flee in panic

Word History

The word *stampede* comes from the Spanish *estampar*, meaning to "to stamp" and was later changed in American-Spanish to *estampida*.

stored (stord) *adj.* past tense of **store:** to put away for future use

strands (strandz) *n.* plural form of **strand:** one of the threads or wires twisted together to form a rope, cord, or cable

streaming (strēm´ ing) *adj.* form of **stream:** a body of flowing water; a steady flow or movement

strive (strīv) *v.* to work to get something

stubborn (stub´ ərn) *adj.* unwilling to change

submerged (səb mûrjd´) *v.* past tense of **submerge:** to cover or overflow with water

> **Pronunciation Key:** at; lāte; câre; fäther; set; mē; it; kīte; ox; rōse; ô in bought; coin; book; too; form; out; up; ūse; tûrn; ə sound in about, chicken, pencil, cannon, circus; chair; hw in which; ring; shop; thin; there; zh in treasure.

success (sək ses´) *n.* the achievement of an aim or purpose

surge (sûrj) *n.* a sudden jerk or strain

suspended (sə spen´ dəd) *v.* past tense of **suspend:** to hang

swarming (swôr´ ming) *v.* form of **swarm:** to gather or live in a large group

sympathetic (sim´ pə the´ tik) *adj.* understanding; having a kind feeling for someone

Word History

Sympathetic comes from the Greek roots *sym,* "together" and *páthos,* "feeling," plus the English suffix *-etic,* "relating to."

tangled (tang´ gəld) *v.* past tense of **tangle:** to wrap in a mess

teeming (tēm´ ing) *v.* form of **teem:** to be full; swarm

tenement (te´ nə mənt) *n.* an apartment that is often run-down and located in a large city

tensely (tens´ lē) *adv.* feeling emotional strain

territory (târ´ ə tor´ ē) *n.* an area of land owned by a country, but whose people do not have the rights of that country

tides (tīdz) *n.* plural of **tide:** the rise and fall of the sea

Word Derivations

Below are some words derived from the word *tide.*

ebb tide	tidal wave	tidemark
high tide	tide table	tides
low tide	tideland	tidewater
tidal	tideless	tideway

timbers (tim´ bərz) *n.* plural of **timber:** a piece of wood forming part of a structure

torrent (tôr´ ənt) *n.* a fast, heavy stream of water or other liquid

trace (trās) *n.* a small bit or sign left behind showing that something was there

tracts (trakts) *n.* plural of **tract:** a piece of land; area

tragic (tra´ jik) *adj.* sad; unfortunate

transferred (trans fûrd´) *v.* past tense of **transfer:** to pass along

transform (trans förm´) *v.* to change from one thing to another

trapper (trap´ ər) *n.* a person whose business is the trapping of animals for their furs

treacherous (tre´ chə rəs) *adj.* full of danger

Word History

The noun *treachery* traces back to Old French *trichier*, "to cheat." *Treacherous* is produced by adding the adjective suffix *-ous*, "having the nature of."

tremendous (tri men´ dəs) *adj.* very large

trickled (tri´ kəld) *v.* past tense of **trickle:** to run slowly in a series of drops or a thin stream

tropical (trä´ pi kəl) *adj.* having warm, moist weather all year due to being near the equator

twitches (twich´ əs) *v.* form of **twitch:** to move with a sudden jerking motion

tycoons (tī kōonz´) *n.* plural of **tycoon:** a wealthy, powerful businessman or businesswoman

typical (ti´ pi kəl) *adj.* average; normal for its kind

understory (un´ dər stôr´ ē) *n.* an underlying layer of vegetation

urchins (ûr´ chənz) *n.* plural of **urchin:** a spiny sea organism

vast (vast) *adj.* large; widespread

venture (ven´ chər) *v.* to dare to go

veteran (ve´ tə rən) *n.* someone who has served in a war

virtual (vər´ chə wəl) *adj.* essence or effect, but not fact or real

weaving (wēv´ ing) *adj.* moving or making by turning and twisting

whack (wak) *v.* to hit sharply

Pronunciation Key: at; l**ā**te; c**â**re; f**ä**ther; s**e**t; m**ē**; **i**t; k**ī**te; **o**x; r**ō**se; **ô** in b**o**ught; c**oi**n; b**oo**k; t**oo**; f**o**rm; **ou**t; **u**p; **ū**se; t**û**rn; **ə** sound in **a**bout, chick**e**n, penc**i**l, cann**o**n, circ**u**s; **ch**air; **hw** in **wh**ich; ri**ng**; **sh**op; **th**in; **th**ere; **zh** in trea**s**ure.

windmills (wind´ milz´) *n.* plural of **windmill:** a machine that uses the power of wind to grind grain or produce eletrical power

windmills

wither (wi´ thər) *v.* to dry up; to shrivel

wren (ren) *n.* a small songbird with brown feathers, a narrow bill, and a short tail that often sticks upward

Z

zigzagging (zig´ zag´ ing) *adj.* having a line, pattern, or course moving in or having a series of short, sharp turns

Reading Resources

Reading Comprehension

Comprehension Strategies will help you understand what you are reading.

Summarizing

As you read, ask yourself the following questions:

1. What is this selection about?
2. How can I state what I have just read in my own words?
3. How should I organize my summary?
4. Have I included any information that should be deleted from my summary?
5. Have I repeated any information that should be deleted from my summary?

Clarifying

As you read, ask yourself the following questions:

1. Does this selection make sense? If not, what do I not understand?
2. If I do not know a word, how can I figure it out? Will word analysis, context clues, or apposition help me figure out the meaning? If I am still confused, should I ask someone or look it up in the dictionary or glossary?
3. If a sentence is long and complicated, have I reread it as well as the sentences before and after it to see if the meaning is clarified? Have I read the sentence part by part to see exactly what is confusing? Have I tried to restate the sentence in my own words?
4. If the paragraph is long and includes many facts and details, have I reread the paragraph more slowly? Have I looked for and found the meanings of words that I do not know? Have I discussed the paragraph with someone to help clarify? Have I tried to restate the information in my own words to make sure that I understand it?

Asking Questions

As you read, ask yourself the following questions:

1. What do I already know about this topic?
2. What else would I like to know about this topic?
3. What questions do I think the author will answer as I read this selection?

4. How does this information connect to what I already know about the topic?

5. How does this information connect to the unit theme?

6. What is not making sense in this selection?

7. What is interfering with my understanding?

Predicting

As you read, ask yourself the following questions:

1. What do I predict will happen next?

2. What evidence from the selection supports my prediction?

3. What evidence from my personal experience or knowledge supports my prediction?

Confirming Predictions

As you read, ask yourself the following questions:

1. How was my prediction confirmed? What information supported my prediction?

2. Was my prediction incorrect or not confirmed? What really happened?

3. What clues did I miss that might have helped me make a more accurate prediction?

Making Connections

As you read, ask yourself the following questions:

1. Does this selection remind me of something else I have read or seen?

2. What personal connections can I make to this selection?

3. How does this selection connect with other selections I have read, either in this unit or other units?

4. How does this selection connect to events in our world today?

5. How does this selection relate to events or topics I have studied in social studies or science?

Visualizing

As you read, ask yourself the following questions:

1. What pictures do the words from this selection create in my mind?

2. What can I see, hear, smell, taste, and/or feel in my mind?

3. Which specific words from the selection help me visualize the feelings, actions, and settings?

4. How does my mental picture help me understand what I am reading?

5. How does the author's descriptions help extend my understanding beyond the text?

Adjusting Reading Speed

As you read, ask yourself the following questions:

1. If I am reading to understand something, how much will I need to slow down to make sure I understand the text?

2. If I am reviewing something I read or studied before, how quickly can I read it? Should I skim the selection until I find something I need to read more carefully?

3. Have I selected the appropriate reading speed to match my purpose for reading?

4. If I do not understand what I am reading, how can I adjust my speed to help me understand and remember what I am reading?

5. Do I need to back up and reread part of the text more slowly?

Comprehension Skills will help you understand the purpose and organization of a selection.

Author's Point of View

Author's point of view explains who is telling the story. When a story is told by a character in the story, it is told in the first-person point of view. The character uses the pronouns *I, my, me,* and *we.* When a story is told in third-person point of view, the story is told by someone who is not part of the story. The pronouns *he/she, him/her, they,* and *it* are used.

Sequence

Sequence is the order in which things happen in a story. The more you know about the sequence of events in a story, the better you will understand the story. Writers use time and order words such as *first, then, finally, tonight,* and *yesterday* to tell the order of events.

Main Idea and Details

The main idea is what the story or paragraph is mostly about. Writers use details to tell more about or explain the main idea.

Compare and Contrast

Compare means "to tell how things, events, or characters are alike." *Contrast* means "to tell how things, events, or characters are different." Writers use compare and contrast to make an idea clearer or to make a story more interesting.

Cause and Effect

Cause-and-effect relationships help you understand connections between the events in a story. The cause is why something happens. The effect is what happens as a result. A cause produces an effect.

Classify and Categorize

An author often includes many details in a story. Putting the like things together, or classifying those like things into categories, helps you see how actions, events, and characters from a story are related.

Author's Purpose

An author writes for different purposes or reasons. An author may write to entertain, to inform, or to persuade. If an author is writing to entertain, he or she might use amusing words or exciting events. If an author is writing to inform, he or she might use facts that can be proved or might explain steps in a process. If an author is writing to persuade, he or she includes his or her opinions about something.

Drawing Conclusions

You draw conclusions when you take information in the selection about a character or an event and use this information to make a statement or conclusion about that character or event.

Making Inferences

You make inferences about characters or events in a story by using information that the author provides and adding it to what you already know. Making Inferences helps you better understand the events in a story.

Fact and Opinion

Writers often use facts and opinions in their writing to make their writing more believable, to explain things, or to persuade readers. A fact is a statement that can be proved to be true. An opinion is something a person or a group feels or believes is true, although others may disagree. Opinions are not necessarily true.

Vocabulary Strategies

Context Clues

When you come to an unfamiliar word in your reading, look for clues in the sentence or in the surrounding sentences. These clues might help you understand the meaning of the word.

Apposition

Sometimes the word is defined within the text. In an apposition, the word is followed by the definition, which is set off by commas.

Word Analysis

Examining the parts of a word can help you figure out the word's meaning. For example, the word *unfriendly* can be broken down into meaningful word parts: the prefix *un-*, the base word *friend*, and the suffix *-ly*. Knowing the meaning of each part will help you come up with the definition "not friendly."

Discussion Strategies

Summarizing

1. I think the main idea is …
2. I think an important supporting detail is …
3. I think the best evidence to support the main idea is …
4. To summarize …
5. I learned …
6. I can conclude …

Clarifying

1. I have a question about …
2. I am still confused about …
3. Does anyone know …
4. Could we clarify …
5. I figured out that …
6. I had difficulty understanding _____ because …
7. I still do not understand …
8. What did the author mean when he or she wrote _____?
9. Who can help me clarify _____?
10. Why did the author _____?

Asking Questions

1. What if …
2. How do we know …
3. I wonder what would happen if …
4. What do we know about …
5. I wonder why the author chose to …

Predicting

1. I expect …
2. I predict …
3. Based on _____ , I predict …
4. I can support my prediction by/with …

5. I would like to change my prediction because …

6. My prediction was confirmed when/by …

7. My prediction was not confirmed because …

Making Connections

1. This made me think …

2. I was reminded of …

3. This selection reminds me of what we read in _____ because …

4. This selection connects to the unit theme because …

5. I would like to make a connection to …

6. I found _____ interesting because …

7. This author's writing reminds me of …

Visualizing

1. When I read _____, I visualized …

2. The author's words _____ helped me visualize …

3. Visualizing helped me understand …

4. The author made the story really come alive by …

Adjusting Reading Speed

1. I decided to read this more slowly because …

2. I found that I needed to slow down when …

3. I found I could skim the material because …

Other Discussion Starters

Personal Response

1. I did not know that …

2. I liked the part where …

3. I agree with _____ because …

4. I disagree with _____ because …

5. The reason I think _____ is …

6. I was surprised to find out …

7. I like the way the author developed the character by …

Agreeing with a Response

1. I agree because …

2. I see what you mean because …

Disagreeing with a Response

1. I disagree because …

2. I think we can agree that _____, but …

Fourth Grade English-Language Arts Content Standards

Reading

1.0 Word Analysis, Fluency, and Systematic Vocabulary Development

Students understand the basic features of reading. They select letter patterns and know how to translate them into spoken language by using phonics, syllabication, and word parts. They apply this knowledge to achieve fluent oral and silent reading.

Word Recognition

1.1 Read narrative and expository text aloud with grade-appropriate fluency and accuracy and with appropriate pacing, intonation, and expression.

Vocabulary and Concept Development

1.2 Apply knowledge of word origins, derivations, synonyms, antonyms, and idioms to determine the meaning of words and phrases.

1.3 Use knowledge of root words to determine the meaning of unknown words within a passage.

1.4 Know common roots and affixes derived from Greek and Latin and use this knowledge to analyze the meaning of complex words (e.g., *international*).

1.5 Use a thesaurus to determine related words and concepts.

1.6 Distinguish and interpret words with multiple meanings.

2.0 Reading Comprehension

Students read and understand grade-level-appropriate material. They draw upon a variety of comprehension strategies as needed (e.g., generating and responding to essential questions, making predictions, comparing information from several sources). The selections in Recommended Literature, Kindergarten Through Grade Twelve illustrate the quality and complexity of the materials to be read by students. In addition to their regular school reading, students read one-half million words annually, including a good representation of grade-level-appropriate narrative and expository text (e.g., classic and contemporary literature, magazines, newspapers, online information).

Structural Features of Informational Materials

2.1 Identify structural patterns found in informational text (e.g., compare and contrast, cause and effect, sequential or chronological order, proposition and support) to strengthen comprehension.

Comprehension and Analysis of Grade-Level-Appropriate Text

2.2 Use appropriate strategies when reading for different purposes (e.g., full comprehension, location of information, personal enjoyment).

2.3 Make and confirm predictions about text by using prior knowledge and ideas presented in the text itself, including illustrations, titles, topic sentences, important words, and foreshadowing clues.

2.4 Evaluate new information and hypotheses by testing them against known information and ideas.

2.5 Compare and contrast information on the same topic after reading several passages or articles.

2.6 Distinguish between cause and effect and between fact and opinion in expository text.

2.7 Follow multiple-step instructions in a basic technical manual (e.g., how to use computer commands or video games).

3.0 Literary Response and Analysis

Students read and respond to a wide variety of significant works of children's literature. They distinguish between the structural features of the text and the literary terms or elements (e.g., theme, plot, setting, characters). The selections in Recommended Literature, Kindergarten Through Grade Twelve illustrate the quality and complexity of the materials to be read by students.

Structural Features of Literature

3.1 Describe the structural differences of various imaginative forms of literature, including fantasies, fables, myths, legends, and fairy tales.

Narrative Analysis of Grade-Level-Appropriate Text

3.2 Identify the main events of the plot, their causes, and the influence of each event on future actions.

3.3 Use knowledge of the situation and setting and of a character's traits and motivations to determine the causes for that character's actions.

3.4 Compare and contrast tales from different cultures by tracing the exploits of one character type and develop theories to account for similar tales in diverse cultures (e.g., trickster tales).

3.5 Define figurative language (e.g., simile, metaphor, hyperbole, personification) and identify its use in literary works.

Writing

1.0 Writing Strategies

Students write clear, coherent sentences and paragraphs that develop a central idea. Their writing shows they consider the audience and purpose. Students progress through the stages of the writing process (e.g., prewriting, drafting, revising, editing successive versions).

Organization and Focus

1.1 Select a focus, an organizational structure, and a point of view based upon purpose, audience, length, and format requirements.

1.2 Create multiple-paragraph compositions:
a. Provide an introductory paragraph.
b. Establish and support a central idea with a topic sentence at or near the beginning of the first paragraph.
c. Include supporting paragraphs with simple facts, details, and explanations.
d. Conclude with a paragraph that summarizes the points.
e. Use correct indention.

1.3 Use traditional structures for conveying information (e.g., chronological order, cause and effect, similarity and difference, posing and answering a question).

Penmanship

1.4 Write fluidly and legibly in cursive or joined italic.

Research and Technology

1.5 Quote or paraphrase information sources, citing them appropriately.

1.6 Locate information in reference texts by using organizational features (e.g., prefaces, appendixes).

1.7 Use various reference materials (e.g., dictionary, thesaurus, card catalog, encyclopedia, online information) as an aid to writing.

1.8 Understand the organization of almanacs, newspapers, and periodicals and how to use those print materials.

1.9 Demonstrate basic keyboarding skills and familiarity with computer terminology (e.g., cursor, software, memory, disk drive, hard drive).

Evaluation and Revision

1.10 Edit and revise selected drafts to improve coherence and progression by adding, deleting, consolidating, and rearranging text.

2.0 Writing Applications (Genres and Their Characteristics)

Students write compositions that describe and explain familiar objects, events, and experiences. Student writing demonstrates a command of standard American English and the drafting, research, and organizational strategies outlined in Writing Standard 1.0.

Using the writing strategies of grade four outlined in Writing Standard 1.0, students:

2.1 Write narratives:
a. Relate ideas, observations, or recollections of an event or experience.
b. Provide a context to enable the reader to imagine the world of the event or experience.
c. Use concrete sensory details.
d. Provide insight into why the selected event or experience is memorable.

2.2 Write responses to literature:
a. Demonstrate an understanding of the literary work.
b. Support judgments through references to both the text and prior knowledge.

2.3 Write information reports:
a. Frame a central question about an issue or situation.
b. Include facts and details for focus.
c. Draw from more than one source of information (e.g., speakers, books, newspapers, other media sources).

2.4 Write summaries that contain the main ideas of the reading selection and the most significant details.

Written and Oral English Language Conventions

The standards for written and oral English language conventions have been placed between those for writing and for listening and speaking because these conventions are essential to both sets of skills.

1.0 Written and Oral English Language Conventions

Students write and speak with a command of standard English conventions appropriate to this grade level.

Sentence Structure

1.1 Use simple and compound sentences in writing and speaking.

1.2 Combine short, related sentences with appositives, participial phrases, adjectives, adverbs, and prepositional phrases.

Grammar

1.3 Identify and use regular and irregular verbs, adverbs, prepositions, and coordinating conjunctions in writing and speaking.

Punctuation

1.4 Use parentheses, commas in direct quotations, and apostrophes in the possessive case of nouns and in contractions.

1.5 Use underlining, quotation marks, or italics to identify titles of documents.

Capitalization

1.6 Capitalize names of magazines, newspapers, works of art, musical compositions, organizations, and the first word in quotations when appropriate.

Spelling

1.7 Spell correctly roots, inflections, suffixes and prefixes, and syllable constructions.

Listening and Speaking

1.0 Listening and Speaking Strategies

Students listen critically and respond appropriately to oral communication. They speak in a manner that guides the listener to understand important ideas by using proper phrasing, pitch, and modulation.

Comprehension

1.1 Ask thoughtful questions and respond to relevant questions with appropriate elaboration in oral settings.

1.2 Summarize major ideas and supporting evidence presented in spoken messages and formal presentations.

1.3 Identify how language usages (e.g., sayings, expressions) reflect regions and cultures.

1.4 Give precise directions and instructions.

Organization and Delivery of Oral Communication

1.5 Present effective introductions and conclusions that guide and inform the listener's understanding of important ideas and evidence.

1.6 Use traditional structures for conveying information (e.g., cause and effect, similarity and difference, posing and answering a question).

1.7 Emphasize points in ways that help the listener or viewer to follow important ideas and concepts.

1.8 Use details, examples, anecdotes, or experiences to explain or clarify information.

1.9 Use volume, pitch, phrasing, pace, modulation, and gestures appropriately to enhance meaning.

Analysis and Evaluation of Oral Media Communication

1.10 Evaluate the role of the media in focusing attention on events and in forming opinions on issues.

2.0 Speaking Applications (Genres and Their Characteristics)

Students deliver brief recitations and oral presentations about familiar experiences or interests that are organized around a coherent thesis statement. Student speaking demonstrates a command of standard American English and the organizational and delivery strategies outlined in Listening and Speaking Standard 1.0.

Using the speaking strategies of grade four outlined in Listening and Speaking Standard 1.0, students:

2.1 Make narrative presentations:
a. Relate ideas, observations, or recollections about an event or experience.
b. Provide a context that enables the listener to imagine the circumstances of the event or experience.
c. Provide insight into why the selected event or experience is memorable.

2.2 Make informational presentations:
a. Frame a key question.
b. Include facts and details that help listeners to focus.
c. Incorporate more than one source of information (e.g., speakers, books, newspapers, television or radio reports).

2.3 Deliver oral summaries of articles and books that contain the main ideas of the event or article and the most significant details.

2.4 Recite brief poems (i.e., two or three stanzas), soliloquies, or dramatic dialogues, using clear diction, tempo, volume, and phrasing.

Photo Credits

Front Cover ©Ann Summa, (bl) ©JUPITERIMAGES/ABLESTOCK/Alamy; 7 (tr) ©Time & Life Pictures/Getty Images, Inc.; 8 (cl) ©David Young-Wolff/PhotoEdit, Inc., (br) ©Thomas & Pat Leeson/Photo Researchers, Inc.; 9 (tr) ©Dwight Kuhn, (br) ©Altrendo/Getty Images, Inc.; 10 (tr) ©Joel W. Rogers/CORBIS, (cl) ©Stock Montage, Inc., (br) ©SuperStock, Inc./SuperStock; 11 (cl) ©Bettmann/CORBIS, (br) ©America/Alamy; 12–13 ©S. Andreas/zefa/CORBIS; 32 courtesy Barbara Massey; 34–35 ©Digital Vision/Alamy; 56 (tr) courtesy Florence B. Freedman, 56 (br) courtesy Doris Ettlinger; 58–59 ©Danita Delimont/Alamy; 76 courtesy John Kanzler; 78–79 ©David W. Hamilton/The Image Bank/Getty Images, Inc.; 80 (bl) ©David Young-Wolff/PhotoEdit, Inc., (br) ©PhotoDisc/Getty Images, Inc.; 81 ©John Giustina/Getty Images, Inc.; 82–83 ©Hulton Archive/ Getty Images, Inc.; 84 ©The Granger Collection; 84–85 ©Time & Life Pictures/Getty Images, Inc.; 86 ©CORBIS; 88–92 ©The Granger Collection; 95 ©Time & Life Pictures/Getty Images, Inc.; 96–97 ©SuperStock, Inc./SuperStock; 98–99 ©Lawrence Migdale/ Photo Researchers, Inc.; 112–113 (bkgd) ©JVL Productions/ Alamy; 114 ©The Jacob and Gwendolyn Lawrence Foundation/ Art Resource; 115 ©Smithsonian American Art Museum, Washington, DC/Art Resource; 122–123 ©Roberto Montenegro; 124 (br) ©Tony Freeman/PhotoEdit, Inc.; 125 ©Royalty-Free/CORBIS; 138 courtesy Neil Waldman; 140–141 ©The McGraw-Hill Companies; 144–145 ©David Young-Wolff/PhotoEdit, Inc.; 146 (t) ©AGB Photo/Alamy; 147 (tr) ©Nick Dolding/The Image Bank/Getty Images, Inc., (b) ©Matt Meadows; 148 ©Frank Siteman/Stone/Getty Images, Inc.; 149 ©Wilbur E. Garrett/National Geographic/Getty Images, Inc.; 151 ©Jim Brandenburg/Minden Pictures; 152 (tl) ©Dennis Kitchen/ Stone/Getty Images, Inc.; 153 (b), 154 (b) ©Matt Meadows; 155 (t) (b) ©Brand X Pictures/Alamy; 156 (cr) courtesy Kimberly Brubaker Bradley; 156–157 ©Yellow Dog Productions/Taxi/ Getty Images, Inc.; 158–159 ©UpperCut Images/Alamy; 160–161 ©SuperStock, Inc./SuperStock; 161 (r) ©Jonathan & Angela Scott/ NHPA; 162–163 ©Steven Kazlowski/Peter Arnold, Inc.; 164 (tl) ©A. Riedmiller/Peter Arnold, Inc., (br) ©James Urbach/SuperStock, (cl) ©National Geographic/Getty Images, Inc.; 165 ©James Zipp/ Photo Researchers, Inc.; 167 ©Clyde H. Smith/Peter Arnold, Inc.; 168 (cl) ©Photographer's Choice/Getty Images, Inc., (br) ©Gary Meszaros/Photo Researchers, Inc.; 169 (tr) ©David Frazier/ PhotoEdit, Inc.; 171 (tr) (br) ©Jack Stein Grove/PhotoEdit, Inc.; 174–175 ©Stone/Getty Images, Inc.; 176–177 ©Thomas & Pat Leeson/Photo Researchers, Inc.; 178 ©James Zipp/Photo Researchers, Inc.; 179, 180–181 ©National Geographic/Getty Images, Inc.; 181 (tl) ©Taxi/Getty Images, Inc., (tr) ©Peter Johnson/CORBIS; 182, 183 ©AnimalsAnimals/Earth Scenes; 184–195 ©Dwight Kuhn; 196–197 (bkgd) ©Peter Arnold, Inc.; 214 (tr) courtesy Lynne Cherry; 216–217 ©Anthony Dunn/Alamy; 218 ©Stone/Getty Images, Inc.; 219 ©Altrendo/Getty Images, Inc.; 220 ©Gregory G. Dimijian, M.D./Photo Researchers, Inc.; 221 ©Jeff Greenberg/PhotoEdit, Inc.; 226–227 ©Burstein Collection/CORBIS; 230–231 ©Joel W. Rogers/ CORBIS; 232 (cr) ©National Oceanic & Atmospheric Administration; 233 ©Linda Robshaw/Alamy; 234 Library of Congress; 234–235 (b) ©Burke/Triolo/Brand X Pictures/Jupiter Images; 235 (tr) ©HIP/Art Resource, (cl) ©Krause, Johansen/Archivo Iconografico, SA/CORBIS; 236 (cr) ©Dave Bartruff/CORBIS; 238 (tl) ©Bettmann/CORBIS; 239 ©Joseph Sohm/Visions of America/CORBIS; 240 ©Stockbyte/ Getty Images, Inc.; 242–243 (bkgd) ©age fotostock/SuperStock; 246–247 ©CORBIS; 248 (bl) ©Royalty-Free/CORBIS, (br) ©Point-of-view/Alamy; 248 (tr), 249 (br) ©North Wind Picture Archives; 250 ©Stock Montage, Inc.; 251 (bc) ©Royalty-Free/CORBIS, (br) ©Comstock Images/Alamy; 252 (tl) ©Neal Mishler/Getty Images, Inc., (tr) ©Stock Montage; 253 (br) ©Bettmann/CORBIS; 254–255 ©Huntington Library/SuperStock; 255 (t) ©The Granger Collection, New York/The Granger Collection; 256 (tr) ©Richard Sobol, (br) ©Bettmann/CORBIS; 256–257 ©North Wind/North Wind Picture Archives; 258–259 ©digital vision/Getty Images, Inc.; 260 (b) ©Bob Daemmrich; 261 ©NASA/CORBIS; 262–263 ©SuperStock, Inc./SuperStock; 263 (br) , 264 (br) ©CORBIS; 264–277 repeating spread (bkgd) ©PhotoDisc/Getty Images, Inc.; 266–267 (c) ©The Granger Collection, New York; 268 (tr) ©Digital Vision Ltd./ SuperStock, (b) ©Getty Images, Inc.; 269 (cr) ©David Muench/ CORBIS, (bl) ©Lowell Georgia/CORBIS; 270 (t) ©David Muench/ CORBIS; 271 (b) ©The Granger Collection, New York; 272–273 (tc) ©Library of Congress; 274 (br) ©The Granger Collection, New York; 276 (bc) ©CORBIS; 278–279 ©Library of Congress; 280–281 (bkgd) ©Stephen Saks Photography/Alamy; 281 (tl) (tr) ©age fotostock/ Superstock; 298 (t) courtesy Laurence Yep, (b) courtesy Scott Goto; 300–301 (bkgd) ©Dr. Parvinder Sethi/The McGraw-Hill Companies, Inc.; 302 ©Lee Foster/Alamy; 303 ©John Elk III/Alamy; 304–305 ©George Steinmetz/CORBIS; 306–307 (bkgd) ©Jim West/Alamy; 307 (tc) ©Bettmann/CORBIS; 308 (t) ©Joseph Sohm/Visions of America/CORBIS; 308–309 (b) ©Ted Soqui/CORBIS; 310 (tr) ©Mark E. Gibson/CORBIS, (b) ©Library of Congress; 310–311 (bkgd) ©Mark Hanauer/CORBIS; 312–313 (bkgd) ©Bettmann/CORBIS, (c) ©CORBIS; 314–315 (b) ©Robert Landau/CORBIS; 316–317 (bkgd), 318–319 (bkgd) ©Joseph Sohm/Visions of America/CORBIS; 320–321 ©America/Alamy.